Do Brilliantly

A2 Physics

Mike Bowen-Jones

Series Editor: Jayne de Courcy

Published by HarperCollins*Publishers* Limited
77–85 Fulham Palace Road
London W6 8JB

www.**Collins**Education.com
On-line support for schools and colleges

First published 2002

ISBN 0 00 712432 5

British Library Cataloguing in Publication Data
A catalogue record for this book is available from the British Library

Edited by Anne Russell
Production by Kathryn Botterill
Design by Gecko Ltd
Cover design by Susi Martin-Taylor
Printed and bound by

Acknowledgements
The Author and Publishers are grateful to the following for permission to reproduce copyright material:

Oxford, Cambridge and RSA Examinations (OCR) (pages 11,17,27,28,32,33–4,39,40,64–5). Answers to questions taken from past examination papers are entirely the responsibility of the author and have neither been provided nor approved by the Oxford, Cambridge and RSA Examinations.

AQA examination questions are reproduced by permission of the Assessment and Qualifications Alliance (pages 10,12–13,22–3,45–6,58–63,73–4,75–6). AQA accepts no responsibility whatsoever for the accuracy or marking of the answers given.

Edexcel Foundation, London Examinations (pages 7–8,16,18,19,24,35,41,42–3,54–6,70–71). Edexcel Foundation, London Examinations, accepts no responsibility whatsoever for the accuracy or method of working in the answers given.

Welsh Joint Education Committee (WJEC) (pages 29,46–7,68–9). Answers to questions taken from past examination papers are entirely the responsibility of the author and have neither been provided nor approved by the Welsh Joint Education Committee.

Illustrations
Gecko Ltd and Roger Penwill

Every effort has been made to contact the holders of copyright material, but if any have been inadvertently overlooked, the Publishers will be pleased to make the necessary arrangements at the first opportunity.

Contents

How this book will help you

by Mike Bowen-Jones

Exam practice – how to answer questions better

This book will help you to improve your A2 Physics grade. It contains lots of actual questions provided for the A2 specifications by AQA, Edexcel, OCR and WJEC.

The different exam boards have different approaches to the second year of the A level course but this book covers the main areas of overlap of all the specifications.

You should have **two aims** in mind in the final stages of preparation for each of your tests or modules. Firstly, **to maximize your knowledge and understanding of the topics** being tested. Secondly, **to ensure that you have good examination technique** so that you can score as many marks as possible with the knowledge that you have. This book will help you to improve your examination technique.

Chapters 1–7 in this book each deal with a major topic. They are broken down into four separate elements, aimed at giving you as much guidance and practice as possible:

1 Exam question, Student's answer and 'How to score full marks'

The questions at the beginning of each chapter are all taken from specimen papers and are typical of what you will be asked. The student's answers are a mixture of **correct responses and common errors.**

The 'How to score full marks' section explains precisely where the student went wrong. I show you how to pick up those vital extra marks that make all the difference between an ordinary grade and a very good one.

2 'Don't make these mistakes'

This section highlights the most common mistakes that students make either in the exam itself or in their preparation for it. When you are into your last minute revision, you can quickly read through all of these sections and make doubly sure that you avoid these mistakes in your exam.

3 'Key points to remember'

These pages list some of the most important facts that you need to know, or definitions that you need to learn for each topic. They are not meant to replace your notes, but are a quick check on those points that it is vital to know before going into your exam. You'll find these pages really helpful with your last minute revision.

4 Questions to try, Answers and Examiner's comments

Each chapter ends with a number of exam questions for you to answer. Don't cheat. Sit down and answer the questions as if you were in an exam. Try to put into practice all that you have learnt from the previous sections in the chapter. I've included, before each question, some exam hints which should help you get the correct answers. Check your answers through and then look at the answers given at the back of the book. These answers give one route that should earn full marks.

In the 'Examiner's comments', I highlight anything tricky about the question which may have meant that you did not get the correct answer. By reading through these comments, you can avoid making mistakes in the real exam.

Synoptic questions

The major difference between AS and A2 exams is that **some of the A2 questions will be synoptic. This means that they are designed to bring together ideas, knowledge and skills from all parts of the specification, including topics that you have studied at AS.**

Synoptic questions are a real test of your ability as a physicist. To succeed, you have to revise more than one topic and you must be prepared to link your understanding of one topic to another.

Chapter 8 explains how you can prepare for synoptic questions. Chapters 9, 10 and 11 give you practice in answering the three types of synoptic questions that are set:

- comprehension questions
- structured questions
- data analysis

For some topics you may find it useful to look back at ***Do Brilliantly: AS Physics*** if you have it on your shelf.

Graphs and Maths

I have also included a chapter called "Graphs and Maths". Although physics questions are never set simply to test maths, it is vital that you should feel confident in using maths in a physics context. For this reason I have spent some time looking at uncertainties and the use of graphs in physics. Each of these topics will crop up in practical work (whether this be an examination or part of course work), but they also provide a skills element which examiners can use as a synoptic link. This, then, is an important chapter for several reasons!

The topics covered by your syllabus

The A2 specifications offered by the four exam boards differ both in the order in which the content is covered and in the content itself. **Chapters 1–7 of this book cover the core content that appears in all the A2 specifications.** (AQA specification A and OCR specification A each offer options; it is not possible to cover the amount of detail required by these options in a book of this type).

Exam Tips

- Many of the exam scripts I mark contain errors that could be avoided if the candidate followed a few relatively straightforward ideas. **Examiners would like you to develop a set of 'good habits' that you apply as 'second nature'**. You can then concentrate on making the most of the physics that you know.
- Questions offering more marks require **more detailed answers** than those worth fewer marks.
- Every numerical answer needs **an appropriate unit** (unless the quantity is 'dimensionless').
- You must communicate your thoughts to the examiner in a **clear way**.
- Don't panic and rush through the exam without taking the time to **think through your answers**.
- **Make sure your handwriting is legible**. The examiner will try hard to read what you have written, but if he or she cannot then you will not gain any marks. Don't forget that, unlike your teacher or tutor, this is the first time the examiner will have seen your handwriting and so you should go all out to make his or her task as easy as possible.
- Take time to **read the set of instructions on the front of the exam paper** that tells you how to approach answering questions. You must follow these instructions precisely.

Here are some of the most common command words used in A2 Physics questions:

State – means that you need to recall a name, a phrase or an equation. It needs no explanation and the answer is usually worth one mark.	**Define** – means that you must recall and write down a formal 'textbook-type' statement. This is likely to be worth either one or two marks.
Explain – requires some detail. You need to give a concise but relevant statement of the meaning of a concept in a manner that is clear and unconfusing. Don't waffle! In physics, it is quite acceptable to 'explain' things mathematically using standard mathematical symbols.	**State and explain** – Questions will often ask you to state and explain something. The 'state' part will probably be worth a mark or two and the 'explain' part the remainder of the marks.
Discuss – usually requires you to consider different aspects of a situation. This type of question is very open-ended and difficult to mark consistently since there is no single 'correct' answer. Questions with this command word are likely to be worth a significant number of marks.	**Describe** – usually relates to experimental techniques and needs no more than a simple description of what you would do, without any supporting reason. Diagrams or sketch graphs will often help to focus your description. Questions with this command word may also be worth a high number of marks.
Sketch – is a term used almost uniquely in physics and requires you to draw the general shape of a graph. You must label the axes with quantities and units (if possible). Be careful to include the origin if it is relevant and any other key points should also be shown. Questions like this may also carry quite high marks.	**Show that** – means that you are given the answer and need to provide the full argument (usually mathematical) that shows why the given answer is correct. You must include a full description of how you reached the answer if you are going to score full marks. These questions are usually worth two or three marks.
Suggest – means that you may not have studied this topic but should be able to come up with a sensible reason or answer based on what you know. There is unlikely to be only one correct answer. These questions may be worth anything between two and a lot of marks. You can tell from the marks available how detailed your answer needs to be.	**Estimate** – means that you are not expected to work to more than one or two significant figures using either rough values provided in the data or else values that you need to make a reasoned 'guess' about. Often these questions require answers that are no more than the correct order of magnitude (power of 10).'Estimate' calculations are not detailed and so are usually worth fewer marks than 'normal' calculations.

Exam question and student's answer

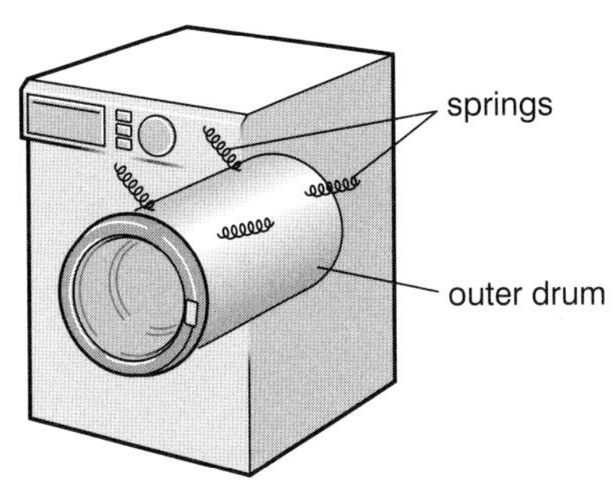

1 Domestic washing machines often incorporate washing, rinsing, spinning and drying. This question is about the spinning.

The inner drum of the machine into which the clothes are placed has quite large holes in it. Explain carefully how, when the clothes are being spin-dried, the water gets from the clothes and out through the holes.

The drum spins at a high velocity. When this happens a centripetal force occurs at right angles to the axis of the drum. Driven by this force the water molecules are forced outside the drum through the holes, whereas clothes are too large to pass through. ✓

[3 marks]

One of the spin speeds in one model of washing machine was listed as 1000 rpm (rpm stands for revolutions per minute). Calculate this spin speed in radians per second.

$\omega = \frac{\theta}{t} = \frac{3600 \times 1000}{60} = 6000 \text{ rad s}^{-1}$ ✗

Spin Speed = 6000 rad s^{-1}

[1 mark]

Calculate the highest centripetal force that could be exerted on a wet sweatshirt of mass $m = 0.5$ kg. The radius of the spinning drum is 12.5 cm.

$F = \frac{mv^2}{r} = mr\omega^2$ ✓ $= 0.5 \times 12.5 \times 10^{-2} \times 6000^2$

Force = 2.25×10^6 N ecf ✓

[2 marks]

If clothes are unevenly distributed in the machine, it vibrates slightly as it rotates. The outer drum within which the spinning drum rotates is attached to the rest of the framework of the washing machine by springs.

Briefly explain the purpose of these springs.

When the spinning drum vibrates, it will rock the outer drum. If there were no springs and the outer drum was to be attached to the rest of the machine, ✓ the shock of the vibrations would not be damped and it would damage the machine. ✓

[2 marks]

For each spring, the spring constant $k \approx 200 \text{ N m}^{-1}$. In use, the loading on each spring is effectively 5 kg.

Explain, with the aid of a calculation, what is likely to happen when an unevenly loaded machine begins to spin the clothes.

$2\pi\sqrt{\frac{5}{200}} = 0.99 \approx 1\text{s}$ = spring time period

[2 marks]

[Total 10 marks]

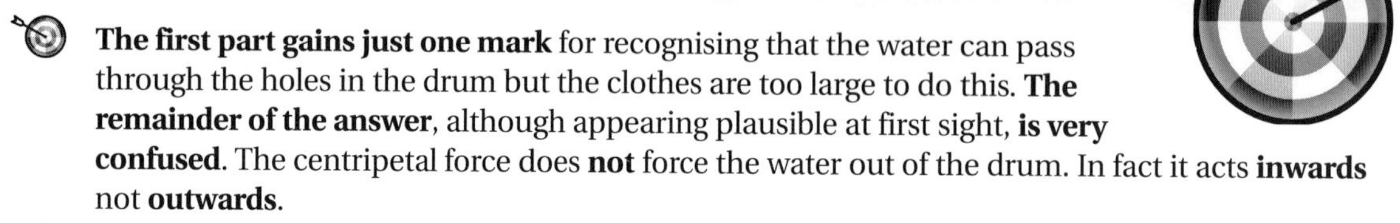

- **The first part gains just one mark** for recognising that the water can pass through the holes in the drum but the clothes are too large to do this. **The remainder of the answer**, although appearing plausible at first sight, **is very confused**. The centripetal force does **not** force the water out of the drum. In fact it acts **inwards** not **outwards.**
- The answer should say that the turning drum exerts a force on the clothes which acts towards the centre of rotation – a centripetal force. No force is possible at the holes and so the water over each hole has nothing to keep it in the circle and it flies off at a tangent to the drum's motion.
- **The second part of the answer is also confused** – the student has converted the angular speed into degrees per second. To convert the number of revolutions per minute to angular speed the number of revolutions must be multiplied by 2π (rev/min → rad/min) and divided by 60 (rad/min → rad/s). **The correct answer is 104.7 rad s^{-1}** (but should be rounded to 2 or 3 significant figures in your answer).
- Although the next answer is not actually correct it does score full marks **because the method is correct** and with the student's value for ω he gets a consistent answer. ('ecf' here means that the student's error is being carried forward and not further penalised.) This means that he has not been penalised twice for a single mistake. The actual value for the centripetal force here should be 685 N.
- The student has made a very good attempt at describing the purpose of the springs and has gained both marks for this.
- In the last part, even though the student has correctly calculated the period, **he has not gone on to explain what might happen** and so fails to gain the second mark. He should have been focused on the idea of resonance (see chapter 2). As the spinning drum accelerates its frequency of rotation will pass through its natural frequency of 1 Hz (corresponding to a period of 1 s) and it will resonate – so its amplitude of vibration will become very large.

Don't make these mistakes ...

Be aware of the difference between radians and degrees. **You rarely work in degrees in circular or simple harmonic motion calculations**. Remember that 360° is equivalent to 2π radians.

Don't give up in a calculation that breaks down. Assume a value and use that for future parts: you will then be given credit – as was this student when he used his incorrect value for ω in the third part of the calculation.

If a question includes the word **explain**, you really do need to give a reason for your suggestion. If you don't, you are bound to lose marks.

Key points to remember

- Uniform motion in a circle means that objects move with **constant speed** (v) around the circle and with **constant angular speed** (ω).
- Although the speed is not changing, the direction is continually changing and so the velocity changes at a constant rate – this means **the object is accelerating**.
- The force that causes this acceleration is called the **centripetal** (centre-finding) **force** – the acceleration is called the **centripetal acceleration**.
- The centripetal force and acceleration are each directed **towards the centre** of the circle.

- The direction of the velocity of the object is along the tangent to the circle at the position of the object.

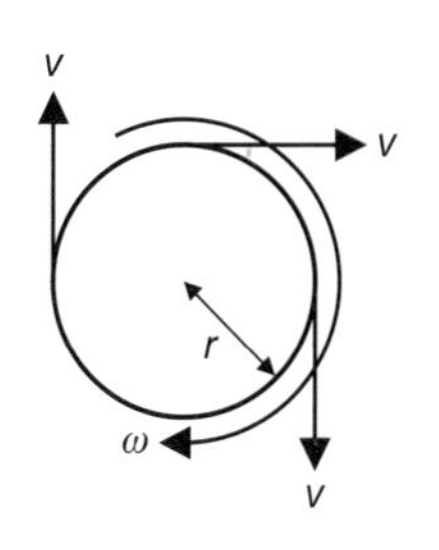

- ω is related to v by the equation:
  $v = \omega r$
  r is the radius of the circle.
- ω is measured in **radians per second** (rad s^{-1})

- There is no single force which is **centripetal** and so **the force should always be labelled with the actual force** providing the centripetal force – weight, reaction, tension, lift, friction (or a component of one of these).
- Much of the difficulty is removed from a calculation when you decide what physical force is acting as the centripetal force.
- Centripetal acceleration is $a = \frac{v^2}{r}$
  centripetal force $= \frac{mv^2}{r} = m\omega^2 r$

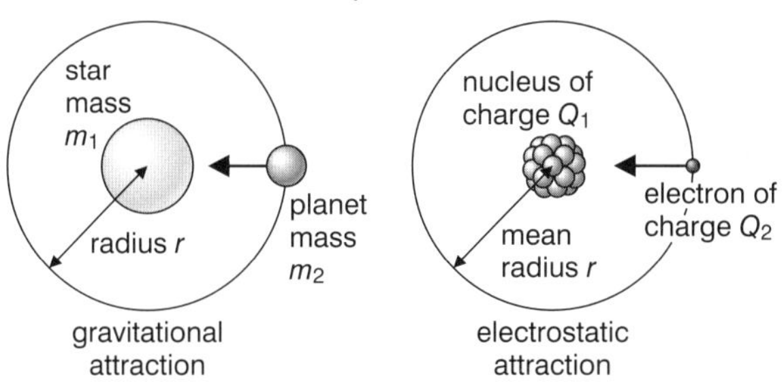

- Gravitation: $G\frac{m_1 m_2}{r^2} = \frac{m_1 v^2}{r}$

  Electrostatics: $\frac{Q_1 Q_2}{4\pi\varepsilon_0 r^2} = \frac{mv^2}{r}$

  where G = gravitational constant, m_1, m_2, m are the masses and Q_1 and Q_2 the charges experiencing the forces. ε_0 is the **permittivity of free space**.
- It is useful to relate the period of rotation to the angular or linear speeds:

  $T = \frac{2\pi}{\omega}$ and $T = \frac{2\pi r}{v}$ (linked by $\omega = \frac{v}{r}$)

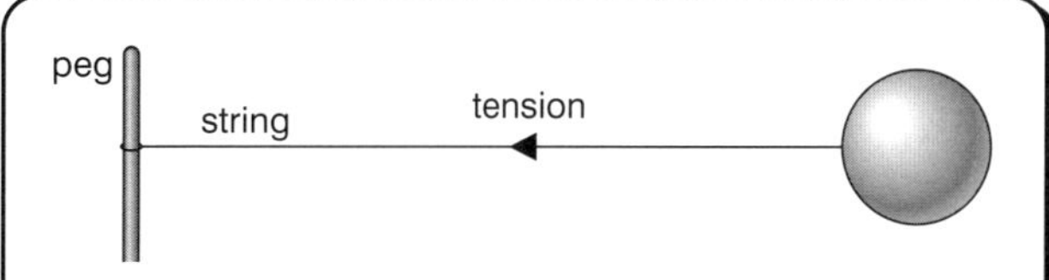

- This figure shows an object being rotated in a horizontal circle – it is moving towards you.
- Since there is no other force acting on the object (in a horizontal plane) the tension is the only force that can provide the centripetal force.
- The weight is acting vertically and would need an upward vertical force to balance it – making a completely horizontal rotation impossible to do in practice (without a surface to hold the object up)!

- This is a more complicated example of circular motion – a weight on a string being whirled in a vertical circle.
- In the position shown the string is not horizontal (where the tension alone provides the centripetal force) and neither at the bottom (where the tension minus the weight provides the centripetal force) nor the top (where the weight plus the tension provides the centripetal force).

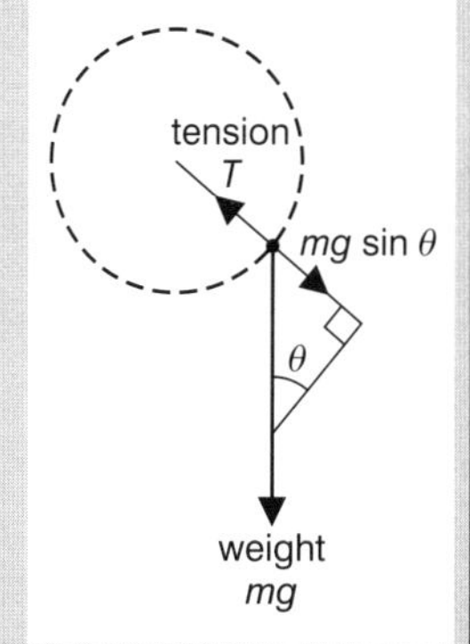

- Here the centripetal force is provided by the tension minus the component of the weight opposite to the tension.
- So $T - mg\sin\theta = \frac{mv^2}{r}$

Questions to try

Examiner's hints for question 1

Part (a) You should think about the link between force and acceleration — in particular the definition of acceleration as the rate of change of **velocity**.

Part (b) Don't forget to answer all of this part – **define your terms**!

Part (c) Although you are not being told what force is providing the centripetal force, you are effectively being told its size – use this information.

Q1

To simulate the high acceleration experienced during take-off, astronauts are trained using a system similar to the one shown in the diagram.

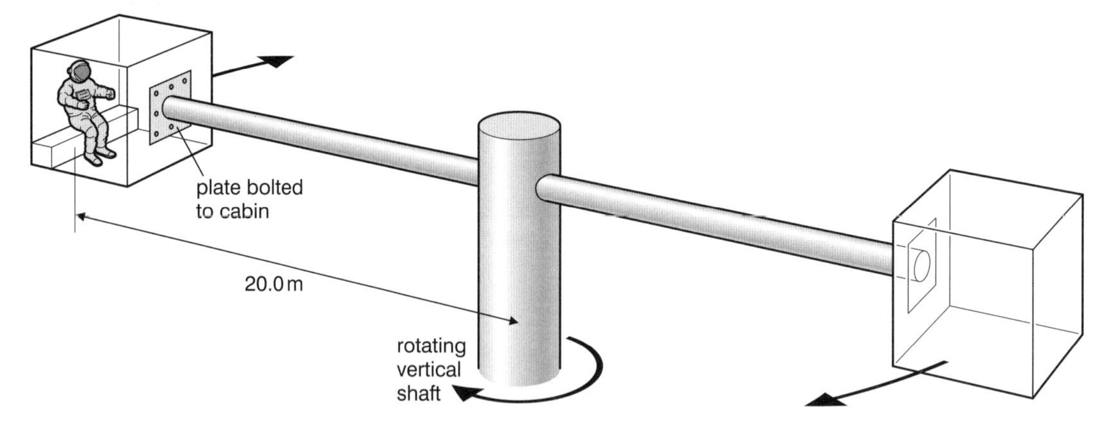

The astronaut sits, as shown, and the system is accelerated to a high speed. The centre of mass of the astronaut is 20.0 m from the axis of rotation.

(a) Explain why there is a horizontal force on the astronaut, even when the speed is constant.

....

....

....

....

....

[3 marks]

(b) Write down the formula for the horizontal force on the astronaut, defining all the terms used.

[1 mark]

(c) In one test the astronaut experiences a horizontal force 4.0 times that due to normal gravity. Determine the speed of the astronaut during this test.

acceleration due to gravity $g = 9.8 \text{ m s}^{-2}$

[2 marks]

[Total 6 marks]

Examiner's hints for question 2
Part (a) Don't forget to label your arrows, as instructed.
Part (b)
(i) A full equation is needed here. **(ii)** Again a full equation.
(iii) This is just Newton's law of gravitation.
Part (c) **(i)** The period is the time that it takes to undergo a full rotation – you need to think about the distance travelled in this time (circumference of the circle), and the relationship between speed, distance and time.
(ii) You need to complete the derivation (showing that T^2 = constant $\times$ r^3).

Q2

A planet P of mass m orbits the Sun S of mass M in a circular orbit of radius r as shown in the diagram.

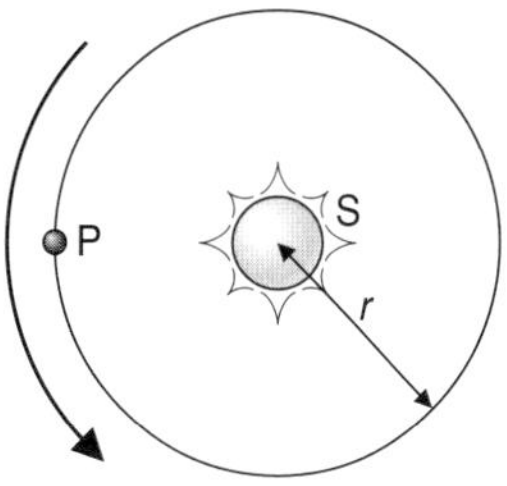

The speed of the planet in its orbit is v.

P S r

(a) On the diagram, draw an arrow to represent the linear velocity of P. Label the arrow V. Draw a second arrow representing the direction of the force acting on P. Label this arrow F.

[2 marks]

(b) **(i)** Write down an expression, in terms of r and v, for the magnitude of the centripetal acceleration of P.

....

[1 mark]

(ii) Write down an expression, in terms of m, r and v, for the magnitude of the force F acting on P.

....

[2 marks]

(iii) Write down an expression, in terms of m, M, r and G, for the magnitude of the gravitational force exerted by the Sun on the planet.

....

[1 mark]

(c) From observations of the motions of the planets around the Sun, Kepler (1571–1630) found that T^2, the square of the period of revolution of a planet around the Sun, was proportional to r^3.

(i) Write down an expression for T in terms of the speed v of the planet and the radius r of its orbit.

....

[1 mark]

(ii) Use your answers to **(b)(ii)**, **(b)(iii)** and **(c)(i)** to show Kepler's relation $T^2 \propto r^3$ would be expected.

....

....

[2 marks]

The answers to these questions are on page 86.

[Total 9 marks]

Exam question and student's answer

1 A simple model of a crystal assumes that the atoms in it are vibrating in the same way as the mass in a mass–spring system such as that shown in the diagram. The inter-atomic bonds behave like the springs and have a 'spring constant' k.

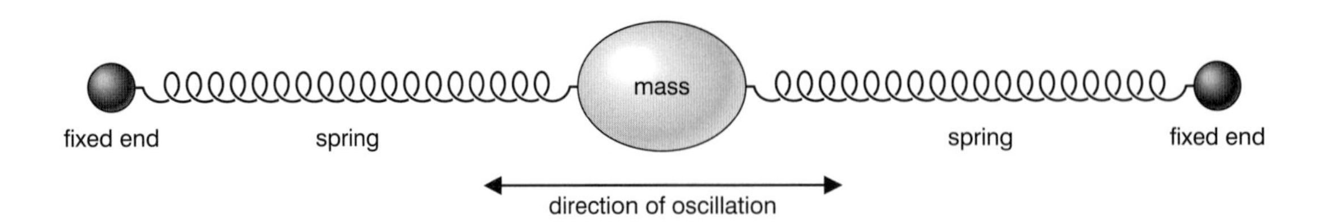

In one instance, an atom in a crystal lattice vibrates with simple harmonic motion of frequency 1.0×10^{13} Hz. The energy of an atom at room temperature is approximately 4.2×10^{-21} J.

(a) Sketch a graph to show how the kinetic energy E_k of the atom varies with displacement from its equilibrium position.

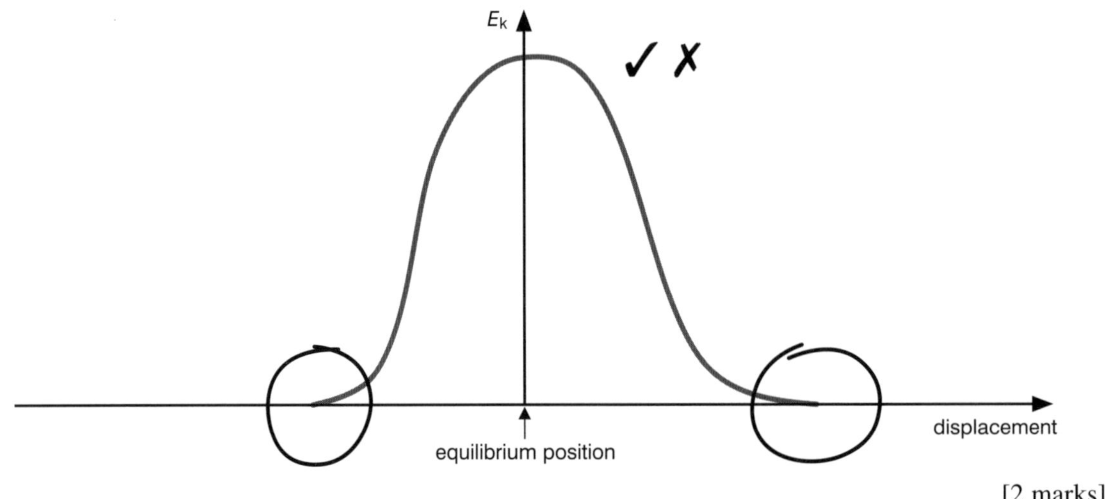

1/2

[2 marks]

(b) (i) Calculate the maximum velocity of an atom of mass 3.7×10^{-26} kg when trapped in a crystal lattice at room temperature.

$$\text{k.e.} = \frac{1}{2} mv^2$$

$$4.2 \times 10^{-21} = \frac{1}{2} \times 3.7 \times 10^{-26} \times v^2 \checkmark$$

$$v_{max} = \sqrt{227027} = 476.5 \text{ m s}^{-1} \checkmark$$

2/2

[2 marks]

(ii) Determine the amplitude of the oscillation of the atom.

$v_{max} = \omega A$

$\therefore A = \dfrac{v_{max}}{\omega} = \dfrac{v_{max}}{2\pi f}$ ✓ $= \dfrac{476.5}{2\pi \times 1 \times 10^{13}} = 7.58 \times 10^{-12}$ m ✓

[2 marks]

(iii) Determine the 'spring constant' k of the inter-atomic bonds holding the atom in the lattice.

$\frac{1}{2}kA^2 = \frac{1}{2}m\omega^2A^2$ ✓

$\therefore k = m\omega^2$ ✓

$= 146$ kg s^{-2} ✓

[3 marks]

(c) When radiation of different frequencies falls on the crystal, one frequency is absorbed because it causes a sharp resonance.

(i) Explain what is meant by *resonance*.

Resonance is when a periodic driving force ✓ is applied to an oscillating system at the same frequency as the natural frequency of the system. ^

[2 marks]

(ii) Explain why atoms are likely to have a sharp resonance whereas resonance of a mass–spring system set up in a laboratory is unlikely to be sharp.

Because the atoms are free ^ it is easier for the driving force to be at the natural frequency. But with the mass–spring system there is a spring connected to the mass therefore it is harder for the driving force to equal the natural frequency. ✗

[2 marks]

9/13

[Total marks 13]

How to score full marks

Part (a)

The basic shape of the curve is of reasonable quality and is a maximum at the correct point. However it needs to be more parabolic than the student has drawn. She has drawn a portion of a $\sin^2$ curve, which is how the energy varies with time, not displacement.

It should be:

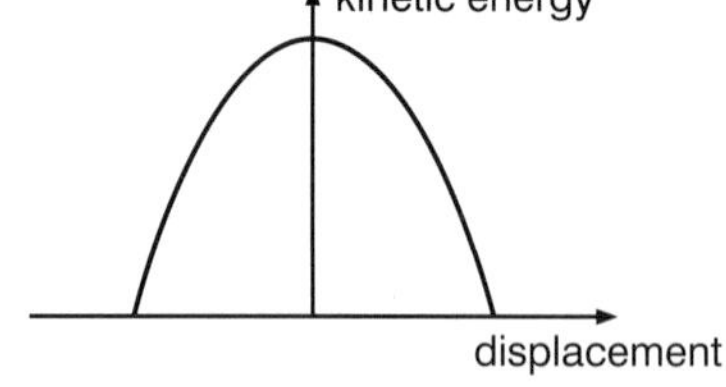

Part (b)

This part is well answered with **calculations clearly laid out**. In part **(i)**, the student has recognised that the energy of the atom will be entirely kinetic when the atom is moving with its maximum velocity and so has equated the atom's energy to $\frac{1}{2}mv^2$.

The maximum velocity should be to rather fewer significant figures than in the answer given. Since all data are to two significant figures it should be expected that answers would be given to this number of significant figures. Although this has not been penalised here, in many cases it would have been. Penalisation of significant figures may depend on the whole paper and so we can assume that this student has been penalised for this elsewhere.

In part **(ii)**, the student recognised that the maximum velocity is equal to the angular frequency times the amplitude and has correctly calculated the amplitude from this.

In part **(iii)**, the student has related the energy stored in the extended spring to the kinetic energy. **She has made her calculation more complicated** than it need be by converting the kinetic energy into an angular form (using $v = \omega r$). If she had used the total energy given in the stem of the question (4.2×10^{-21} J), she could have reached the same answer for k more quickly!

Part (c)

(i) This answer is good but **incomplete. It is a common mistake to give the condition for resonance without stating the effect.** To complete the answer it should say, "....and the amplitude of the oscillation becomes much larger."

(ii) **This answer is classic waffle!** The student does not know the answer and has written something on the off chance that she might scrape a mark. She has not used the hints in the question to help her. She should have thought about what makes a resonance curve less sharp – damping – and then focused on what causes damping in the "mass" system – air resistance (or another frictional force, depending upon what the mass actually is).

The examiners were expecting an answer such as "Atoms will not experience frictional forces (such as air resistance) but a much larger mass would do. Frictional forces cause damped oscillations and reduce the sharpness of resonance."

Don't make these mistakes...

Don't use an unrealistic number of significant figures – you gain no credit from doing so and it shows examiners that you have **not considered any uncertainties** that occur in measurements. You will certainly be penalised at some point in an examination if you do work to too many (or too few) significant figures.

Try to avoid waffling. It is easy to panic and feel that you must write something down for "explain" type questions. Don't fall into the trap of just writing anything. **There will always be hints in the question** – try to think your way through finding out what they are.

Key points to remember

Simple harmonic motion:

- is motion which is periodic and the period is independent of the amplitude;
- is defined by the equation

  $a = -\omega^2 s$

  a is the acceleration in m s^{-2}, ω is the angular frequency in rad s^{-1} and s is the displacement in m.

This means that the acceleration is always proportional to the displacement from a fixed point and is directed towards that point (– sign).

The simple pendulum

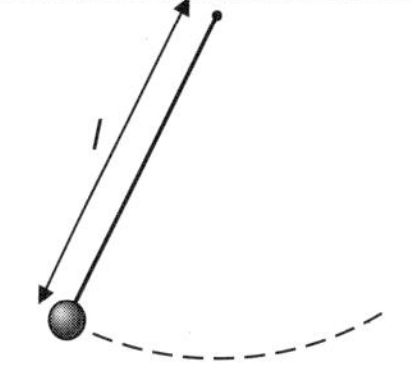

The period of a simple pendulum is given by:

$$T = 2\pi\sqrt{\frac{l}{g}}$$

The period, T, is the time taken to complete one oscillation. It is measured by timing a large number of oscillations and dividing the time by the number of oscillations. Note that it does not depend on the mass of the bob but it does depend on length and gravitational field strength.

- $T = \frac{1}{f}$ (f is the frequency, in Hz, T is in seconds)

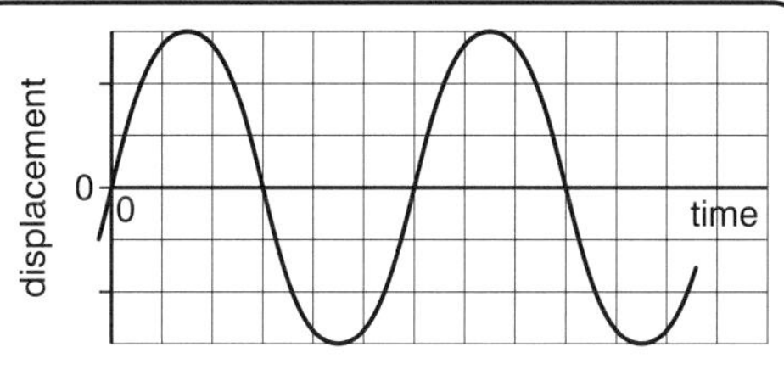

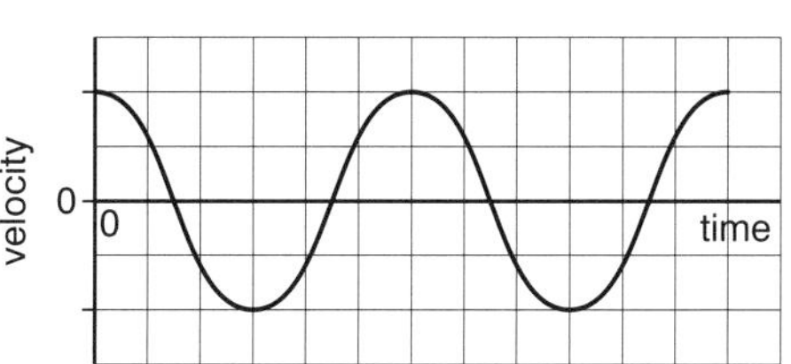

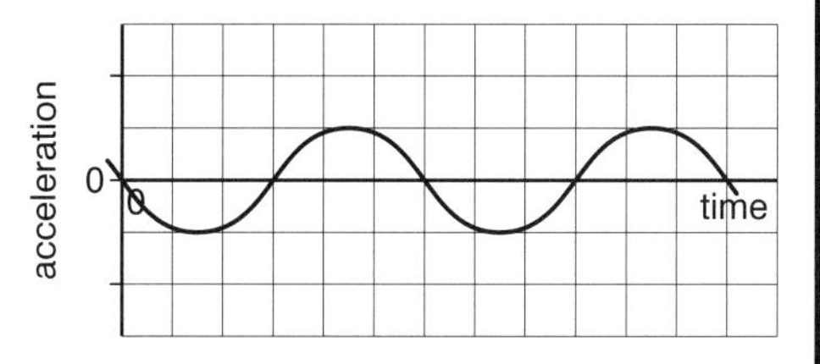

- At any point the gradient of the displacement against time graph gives the velocity at that time.
- The gradient of the velocity against time graph gives the acceleration.
- The acceleration value is always a negative constant multiplied by the displacement value at that time.
- The maximum velocity is given by:

  $v_{max} = \omega A$ (A is the amplitude or maximum displacement).
- The maximum acceleration of magnitude $a_{max} = \omega^2 A$.

The mass is shown in the rest position here.

The period of a loaded spring is given by:

$$T = 2\pi\sqrt{\frac{m}{k}}$$

k is the spring constant (force divided by extension) in N m^{-1}.

- For a spring, ω is given by $\omega = \frac{2\pi}{T} = \sqrt{\frac{k}{m}}$

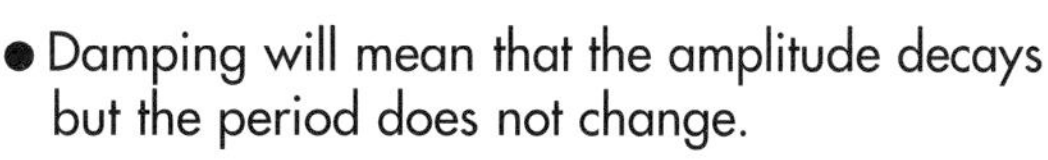

- Damping will mean that the amplitude decays but the period does not change.

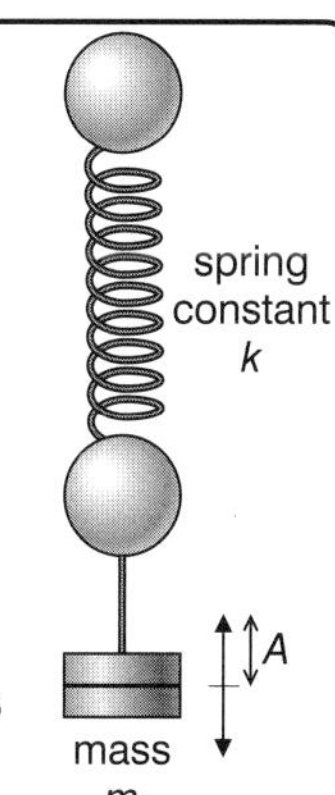

Resonance

- Resonance occurs when the applied frequency is equal to the natural frequency of a system.
- It causes a significant increase in the amplitude of the system to which the energy is being fed in.
- The energy gained by the system that is made to resonate originates from the driving system (i.e. the one providing the applied frequency).

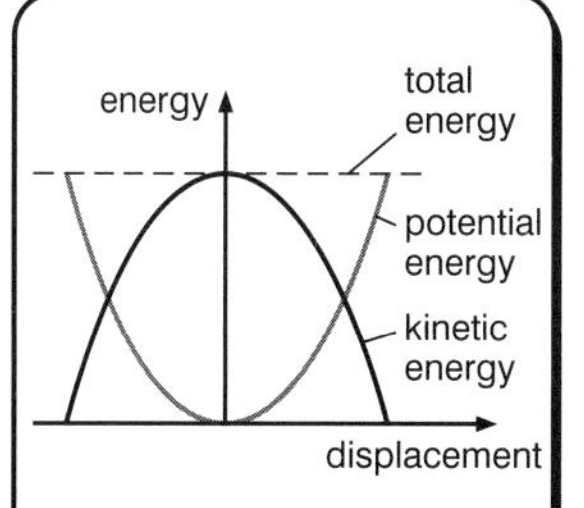

At any displacement the total energy (i.e. the sum of the potential and kinetic energies) is constant.

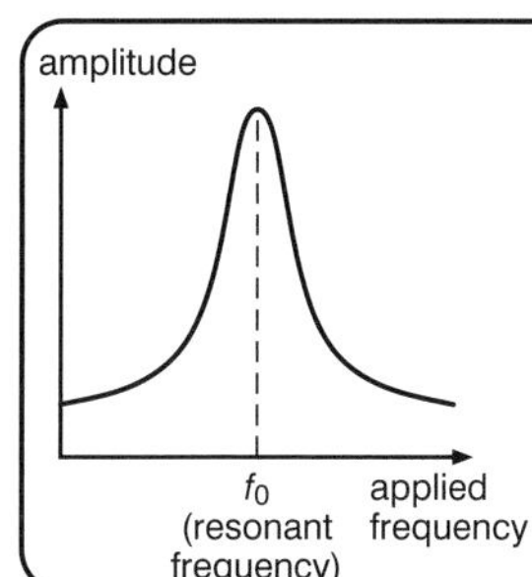

- You should mark the actual value of the resonant frequency on your graph – if you know the value.
- The sharpness of the resonance curve indicates how heavy the damping is – in this case it is quite lightly damped because the peak is quite sharp.

Questions to try

Examiner's hints for question 1

- This question aims to make you think your way through simple harmonic motion. You need to be sure of the equation for maximum acceleration, and think about the relationship between acceleration and displacement (in particular, where they are **both** zero or maximum).

The diagram shows one piston of an internal combustion engine.

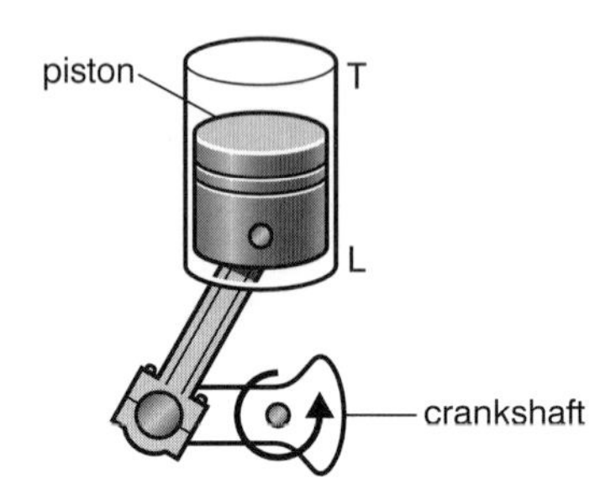

As the crankshaft rotates through 360°, the top of the piston moves from L to T and back to L. The distance LT is 8.6 cm and the crankshaft rotates at 6000 revolutions per minute.

Calculate the frequency of oscillation f of the piston.

f = ...

[1 mark]

State the amplitude of this oscillation.

....

[1 mark]

The oscillations of the piston are approximately simple harmonic. Calculate the maximum acceleration of the piston.

....

....

....

Acceleration = ...

[2 marks]

At which position(s) in the movement of the piston will this acceleration be zero?

....

[1 mark]

[Total 5 marks]

Examiner's hints for question 2
Part (a) (i) Be careful when drafting the oscillation: you will need to show at least three cycles to make the damping evident.
(ii) There are two marks for this so you will need to make two points:
velocity is found by ......
and the change in velocity can be seen because ....
Part (b) You can see where each of the marks are coming from because the question is phrased in order to force you to answer each aspect. Think of the question broken down as:
(1) Name a situation in which damping is necessary.
(2) What (force) causes the damping?
(3) What would happen if there was no damping?

Q2

This question is about damping.

(a) (i) Sketch a graph for a damped oscillation.

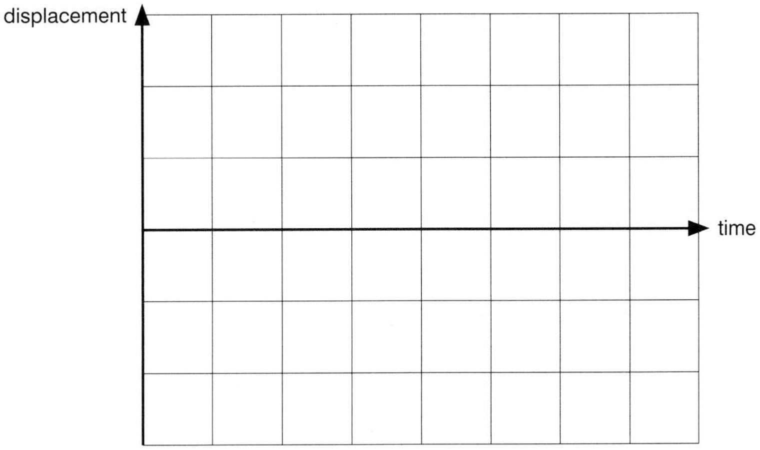

displacement

time

(ii) How does the graph show any changes in velocity?

....

....

[4 marks]

(b) Suggest a situation in which some damping would be desirable. Explain the origins of the damping and the benefits of the damping of an oscillating system in the case you choose to discuss.

....

....

....

....

[3 marks]

[Total 7 marks]

Examiner's hints for question 3

- In the first part the "state" means that the examiners are not expecting a significant calculation. Nevertheless you cannot read *frequency* directly from the graph.
- The second part is more difficult than if you had been given the velocity curve and been asked to draw the acceleration curve (which would have been given by the gradient of the velocity–time curve at each point). Here you may think in terms of the curve that is drawn being the gradient of the curve that you are to draw!
- The last part is a typical A-level skill. Write down the equation for the period in terms of *k* and *m* and then rewrite it for the new period in terms of 2*m* and 4*k*. After that it's algebra!

Q3

A body performs simple harmonic oscillations.

The graph shows how the acceleration *a* of the body varies with time *t*.

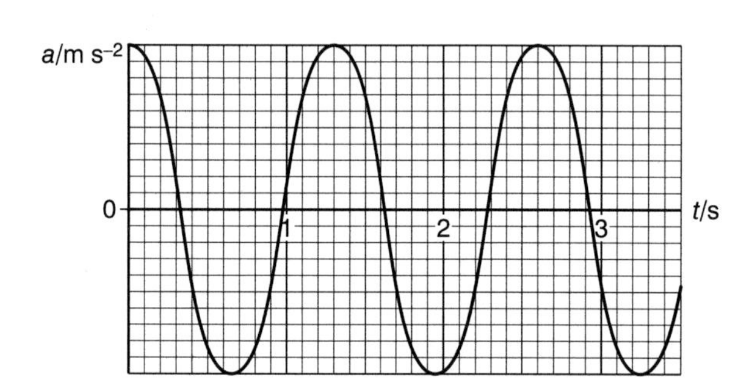

State the frequency of the oscillations.

....

[1 mark]

Add to the graph a curve showing how the *velocity* of the same body varies with time over the same period.

[2 marks]

On the grid below, sketch a graph to show how the force *F* acting on the same body varies with time over the same period.

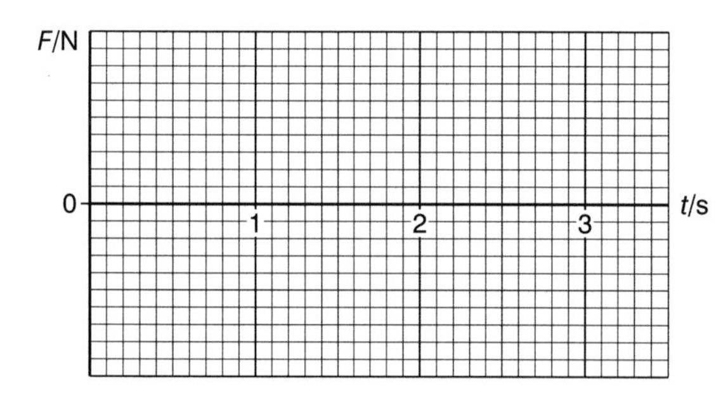

[2 marks]

A mass *m* attached to a spring of force constant *k* oscillates with a period of 1.2 s.

Calculate the period of oscillation for a mass 2*m* attached to a spring of force constant 4*k*.

....

....

....

Period of oscillation = ...

[2 marks]

[Total 7 marks]

The answers to these questions are on pages 86 and 87.

Exam question and student's answer

The diagram (not to scale) shows a satellite of mass m_s in circular orbit at speed v_s around the Earth, mass M_E. The satellite is at a height h above the Earth's surface and the radius of the Earth is R_E.

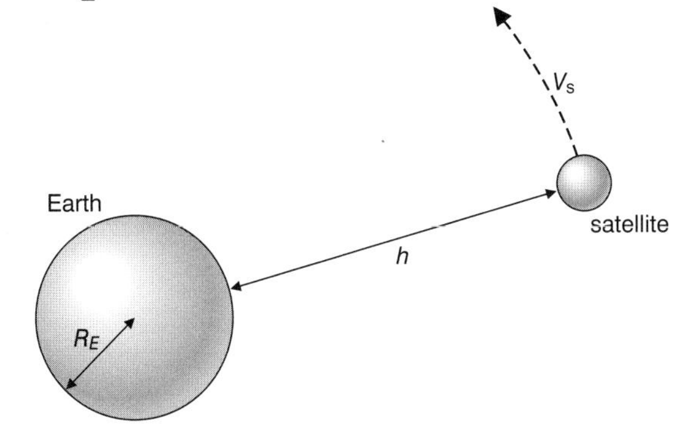

Explain why, although the speed of the satellite is constant, its velocity varies.

The direction is changing

∴ velocity varies

0/1

[1 mark]

Using the symbols above, write down an expression for the centripetal force needed to maintain the satellite in this orbit.

$$F = \frac{M_s v_s^2}{R_E + h}$$ ✓ ✓

2/2

[2 marks]

Write down an expression for the Earth's gravitational field strength in the region of the satellite.

$$g = \frac{F}{M} = \frac{G M_s M_E}{(R_E + h)^2 M_s} = \frac{G M_E}{(R_E + h)^2}$$ ✓ ✓

2/2

State an appropriate unit for this quantity.

N kg^{-1} ✓

1/1

[3 marks]

Use your two expressions to show that the greater the height of the satellite above the Earth, the smaller will be its orbital speed.

$$\frac{M_s V_s^2}{R_E + h} = \frac{G M_E M_s}{(R_E + h)^2}$$

$$V_s^2 = k\frac{1}{(R_E + h)}$$

2/3

$$V_s = k\frac{1}{\sqrt{h}}$$

[3 marks]

7/9

[Total 9 marks]

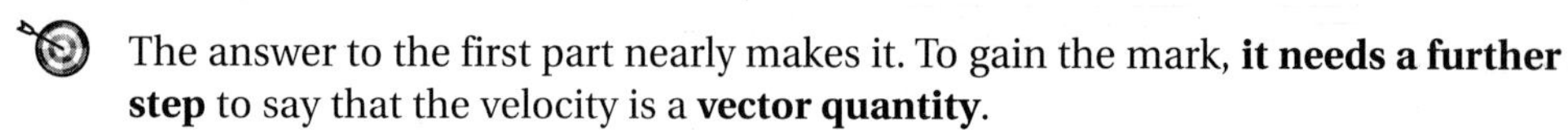

How to score full marks

- The answer to the first part nearly makes it. To gain the mark, **it needs a further step** to say that the velocity is a **vector quantity**.
- The next three parts are very well answered. The student has converted the standard way that the equations are written into those specifically set out in the question.
- Although the final calculation is nearly all correct **the student has made a mathematical error**. He has gone from a correct relationship:

$$v_s^2 = k\frac{1}{R_E + h}$$

and then written

$$v_s = k\frac{1}{\sqrt{h}}$$

which is a mathematically incorrect step. After the next to last equation the student should have stated that **since R_E is constant, increasing h would decrease v_s^2 and therefore v_s.** In his answer the student has shown all the mathematics very clearly – but when he made a slip he was penalised, **because he didn't explain what he was thinking**.

Don't make these mistakes ...

Always use the symbols that are set out in the question. If you change to your own, or even the more usual ones in which you remember equations, you could lose marks. For such a simple thing it is not worth taking the risk!

Do support what you write mathematically with a few words of description – unless the mathematics is extremely straightforward and obvious. When the examiner is left to make a deduction from what you have written, you cannot be given credit. The examiner can't be sure that you understand any deductions yourself – that's why you are sitting the exam in the first place!

Key points to remember

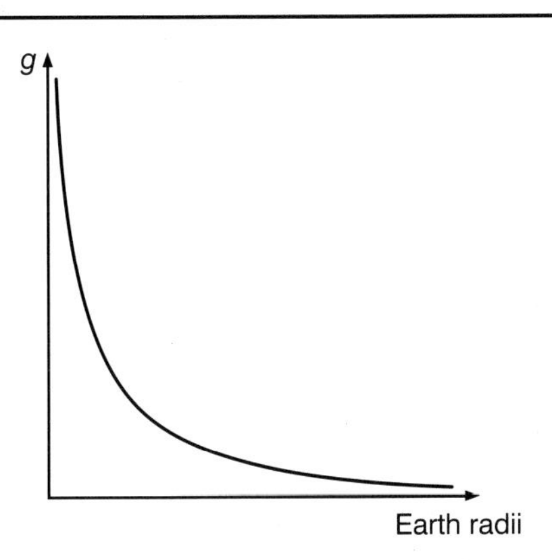

- The shape of the graph above can be generated by taking just a couple of values: as the radius doubles the gravitational field strength decreases to a quarter of its initial value.

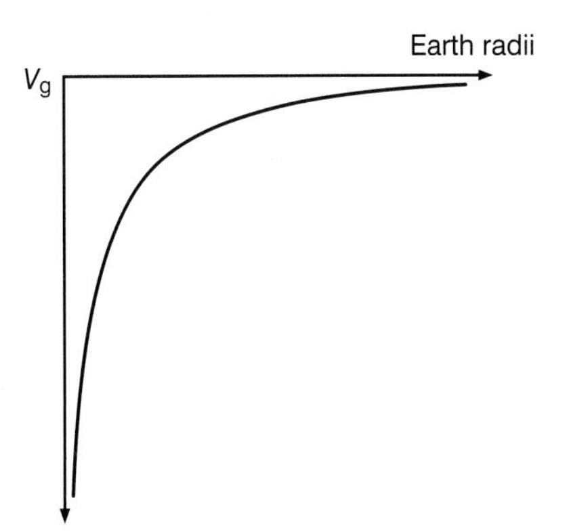

- The area under this graph gives the potential energy per unit mass gained or lost by moving an object between two points – this is **the change in gravitational potential**.
- To check your graph, values of the product $V_g r$ (for corresponding values of V_g and r) should give a **negative constant.**

Gravitational Field Strength (*g*)

- Don't mix this up with G.
- This is the force per unit mass at a point in a gravitational field.
- $g = \frac{F}{m}$
- At the surface of the Earth g is about 9.8 N kg^{-1}.
- At a point in a field generated by an object of mass m:

$$g = G\frac{M}{r^2}$$

- **Newton's law of gravitation** applies to all objects.
- The force between two objects acts on each object and is proportional to the product of their masses ($m_1 \times m_2$).
- The force on each object is **inversely proportional** to the square of the distance between the two centres of mass of the objects ($\propto \frac{1}{r^2}$).
- $F = G\frac{m_1 m_2}{r^2}$

  G is the **universal gravitational constant** $= 6.67 \times 10^{-11}$ N m^2 kg^{-2}
- The force is independent of the material between the two objects that are acting on each other.

- **Gravitational potential energy (g.p.e.)** of a mass at a point in a gravitational field is the work done in bringing a mass from infinity to the point.
- The g.p.e. at infinity is defined as being zero and so the system always does work in attracting the mass (gravitation always provides an attractive force). Thus g.p.e. **is negative anywhere else but at infinity**.
- g.p.e. $= -G\frac{m_1 m_2}{r}$
- Don't use g.p.e. = mgh unless the object is very close to the surface of the Earth.
- **Gravitational potential**, V_g, is the g.p.e. per unit mass so:

$$V_g = -G\frac{M}{r}$$

Question to try

Examiner's hints

- Before you attempt this question, read it through completely. You need to do this to establish the context of the question – this will help you in **part (a)(iii)** for example.
- There are two possible correct answers to **(a)(iii)**; either would gain you credit – you may think of them both. If they are not contradictory, write them both down.
- **Parts (b)(i)** and **(ii)** are "show that" questions; your working must be shown clearly here. In part (ii) the minimum number of points that you should use is two. Choose points that you can read conveniently (whole number of R values, for example). Do not forget the 10^7 factor on the R scale.
- Graphical calculations usually require you to measure gradients or areas. You should think which is appropriate for calculating potential energy from a force/distance graph in **part (b)(iii)**.
- Centripetal forces crop up in circular motion (see chapter 1). You will need to consider which version of the centripetal force equation (i.e. the "v" one or the "ω" one) you need for **part (b)(iv)**.
- **Part (b)(v)** requires you to think about **all** the energy changes that occur when the rocket moves the satellite to a higher orbit.

Q1

(a) A rocket takes off from the Earth. Exhaust gases are discharged vertically downwards causing the rocket to accelerate vertically upwards.

Figure 1 is a sketch graph of the velocity of the rocket against time after lift off.

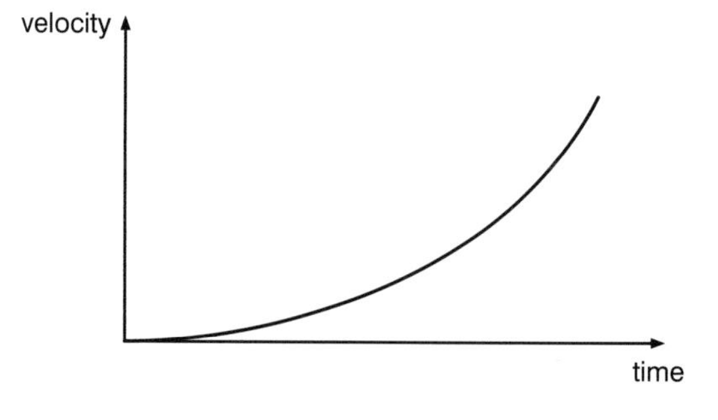

Figure 1

(i) Describe the acceleration of the rocket during the time shown in **Figure 1**.

....

[1 mark]

(ii) By referring to the graph in **Figure 1**, explain your answer to (i).

....

[1 mark]

(iii) Suggest why the rocket accelerates as you have described.

....

[1 mark)]

(b) A satellite has a mass of 3.9×10^3 kg. Initially, it is placed in an orbit of radius 1.0×10^7 m around the Earth.

(i) Show that the centripetal force provided by gravitational attraction is 1.6×10^4 N.

universal gravitational constant, $G = 6.7 \times 10^{-11}$ N m^2 kg^{-2}
mass of the Earth = 6.0×10^{24} kg

[2 marks]

(ii) **Figure 2** shows the variation of the gravitational force F on the satellite with orbital radius R.

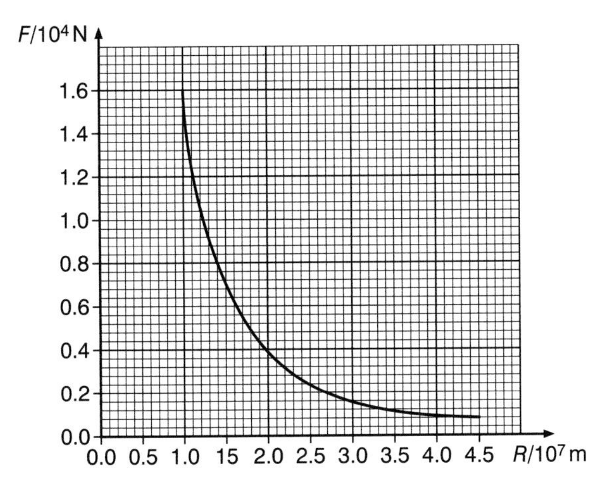

Figure 2

Show that the data given in **Figure 2** are consistent with the inverse square law for the variation of force with distance.

[3 marks]

(iii) Use data from **Figure 2** to find the change in potential energy which occurs when the satellite is raised from its orbit of radius 1.0×10^7 m to an orbit of radius 4.5×10^7 m.

[3 marks]

(iv) When the radius of the orbit is 4.0×10^7 m, the centripetal force on the satellite is 4.5×10^3 N. Calculate the speed of the satellite.

[2 marks]

(v) State and explain whether energy transformed from chemical energy as the fuel burns is equal to the change in potential energy which occurs when the radius of the orbit is increased.

[3 marks]

[Total 16 marks]

The answer to this question is on pages 87 and 88.

Exam question and student's answer

1 Write down an equation for the force between two point charges, Q_1 and Q_2, separated by a distance *r*.

$$F = \frac{Q_1 Q_2}{4\pi\varepsilon_0 r^2}$$ ✓

[1 mark]

A speck of dust has a mass of 1.0×10^{-18} kg and carries a charge equal to that of one electron. Near to the Earth's surface it experiences a uniform downward electric field of strength 100 N C^{-1} and a uniform gravitational field of strength 9.8 N kg^{-1} .

Draw a free-body force diagram for the speck of dust. Label the forces clearly.

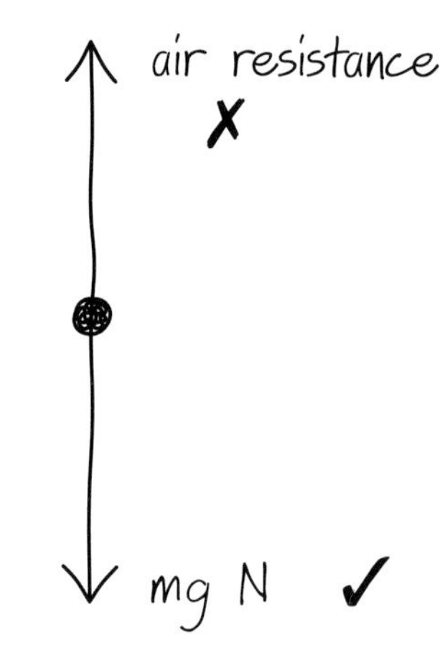

Calculate the magnitude and direction of the resultant force on the speck of dust.

$F = Eq$

$= 100 \times 1.6 \times 10^{-19}$

$= 1.6 \times 10^{-17}$ N ✓

$F = mg$

$= 1 \times 10^{-18} \times 9.8$

$= 9.8 \times 10^{-18}$ ✓

Magnitude of force = 6.2×10^{-18} N ✓

Direction of force = upwards ✓

4/4

[6 marks]

[Total 7 marks]

How to score full marks

- The first part required Coulomb's law for point charges and this is clearly shown, **using the symbols indicated in the question**.
- Despite clearly labelling two reasonable forces, the student gains only one out of the two marks available. **She has completely ignored the fact that the electric field strength is given.** Since this field is downwards (direction of force on a positive charge) and the dust particle is negatively charged, the electric force will be upwards. So she should have shown the forces as:

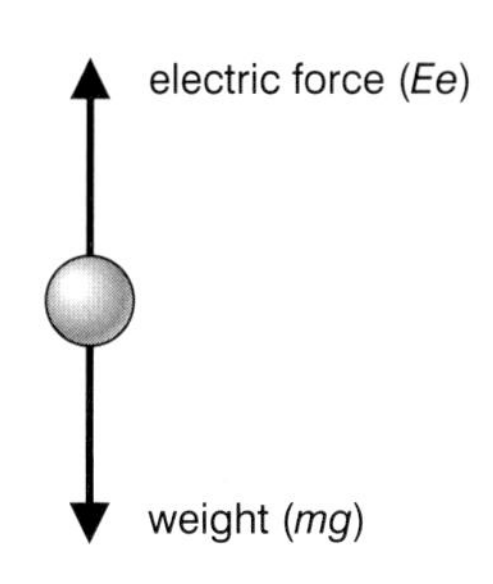

- The final part of the question is totally correct and this should have prompted the student to re-examine her previous answer (which is now seen to be contradictory). **Although she was correct in recognising that the air resistance acting on a speck of dust would be significant, the speck of dust would be moving upwards. Air resistance would oppose the motion of the dust and would, therefore, act downwards.**

Don't make these mistakes ...

When a latter part of a question throws up an answer that is contradictory to an earlier one, do try to resolve the problem. Clearly, **contradictory answers cannot both be correct and this should prompt you to re-evaluate your answers**. However, if your time is short, you should cut your losses and continue with further questions – highlighting the fact that you may wish to return to the earlier part **if you have time**.

Do try to plan your time throughout the exam. You should enter the exam with a very good idea of the time that you should spend on each section of the paper or even each question. You should also know the **number of marks per minute** that you should score and check where you are every 20 minutes or half hour.

Do build into your **marks per minute total sufficient time to check that you have completed the exam and to review any areas that you highlighted** for a second look.

Key points to remember

- **Electric fields** are regions in which a charge experiences a force.
- They are represented by a number of **lines of force**; each starting on a positive charge and ending on a negative charge.
- A point charge (or spherical conductor) has an associated radial field shown as:

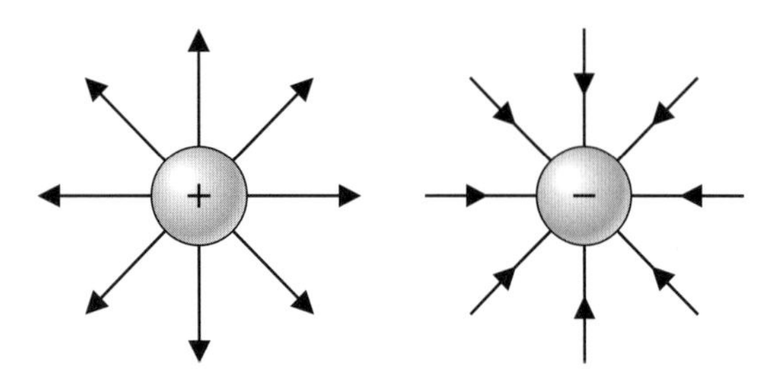

- The electric field strength, E, is given by the force per unit charge on a small test charge placed in the field. It has units of N C^{-1} **or** V m^{-1}.
- $E = \frac{F}{Q}$
- The electric field at a distance r from a point charge is the rate of change of potential at that point, or **potential gradient**.

  $E = \frac{\Delta V}{\Delta r}$
- A pair of parallel charged plates produces a uniform field:

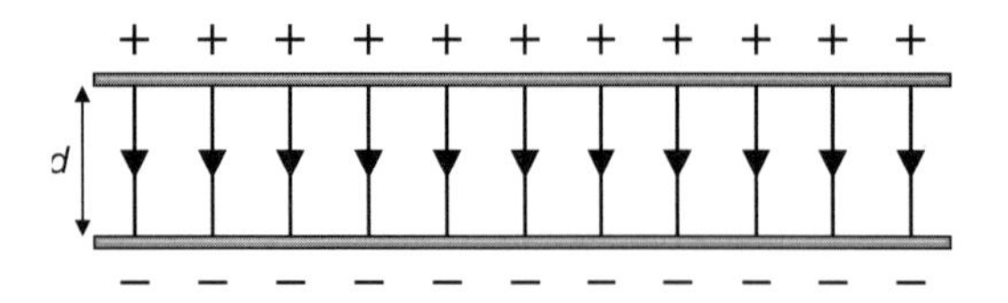

- For a uniform field

  $E = \frac{V}{d}$

  where V is the p.d. across the plates in volts and d is their separation in metres.

- Coulomb's law for point charges relates the force, F, between two charges of size Q_1 and Q_2 to their separation, r, by

$$F = \frac{Q_1 Q_2}{4\pi\varepsilon_0\varepsilon_r r^2}$$

- ε_0 is the permittivity of free space (8.85×10^{-12} F m^{-1}) and ε_r is the relative permittivity of the surrounding medium (for air $\varepsilon_r = 1$)
- This is an inverse square relationship taking the shape:

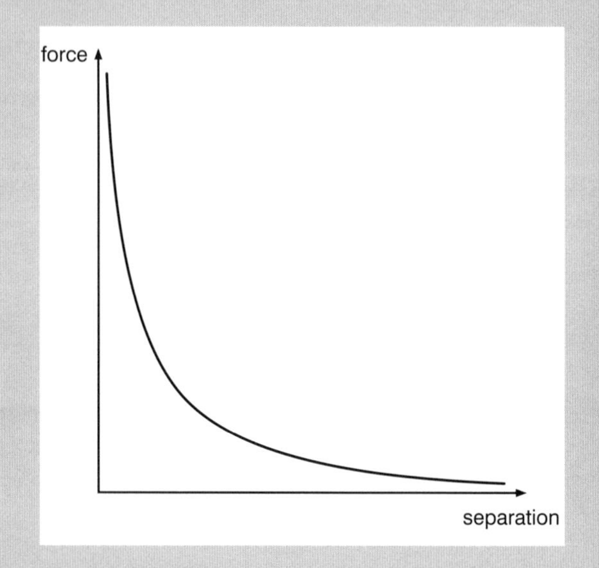

- The electric field strength in a radial field is given by the force per unit positive charge and so takes the same shape as the force separation curve.
- $E = \frac{F}{Q} = \frac{Q}{4\pi\varepsilon r^2}$
- Here $\varepsilon = \varepsilon_0\varepsilon_r$
- Attractive forces are conventionally negative and so when the source of the field is a negative charge, the force will be negative.
- Electric potential (V) at a point in an electric field is defined as the work done in bringing a charge of +1C from infinity to the point.
- $V = \frac{Q}{4\pi\varepsilon r}$

Questions to try

Examiner's hint for question 1

- Electric field strength is also known as the potential gradient.

The graph of electric potential against distance for a nucleus, modelled as a small point charge, is as shown.

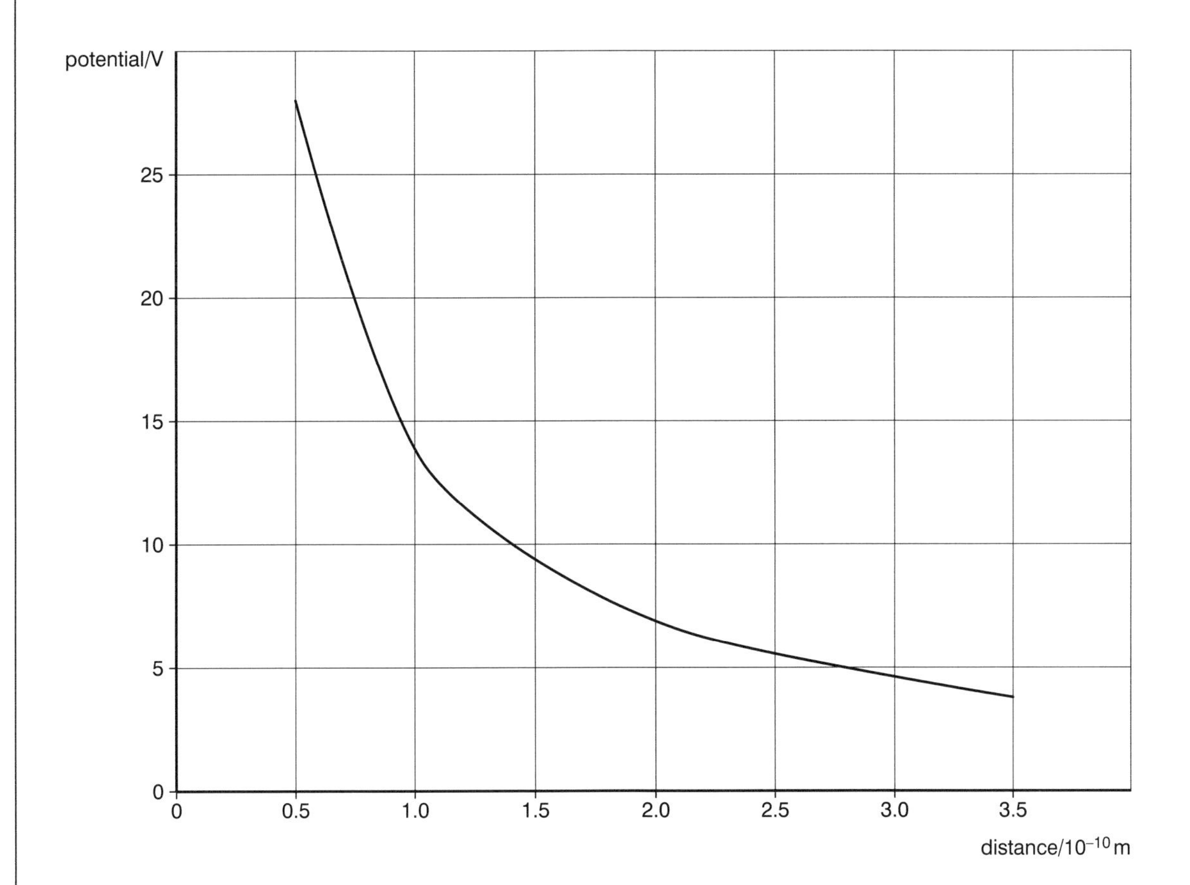

Use the graph to calculate the electric field strength due to this charge at a point 1.5×10^{-10} m from it.

[2 marks]

Examiner's hints for question 2

- **Part (a)** is a little vague but you should be thinking in terms of what the purpose of drawing in field lines is – i.e. what information do you communicate by doing this?
- In **part (b)(i)** this is very much like a parallel plate capacitor although there are no "ends" included here. Again think of the relationship for the electric field with a pair of charged parallel plates.

Q2

(a) State two pieces of information that can be deduced from drawings of electric field lines.

1. ....

2. ....

[2 marks]

(b) The diagram illustrates some of the electric charges in a thundercloud and on the surface of the Earth beneath it.

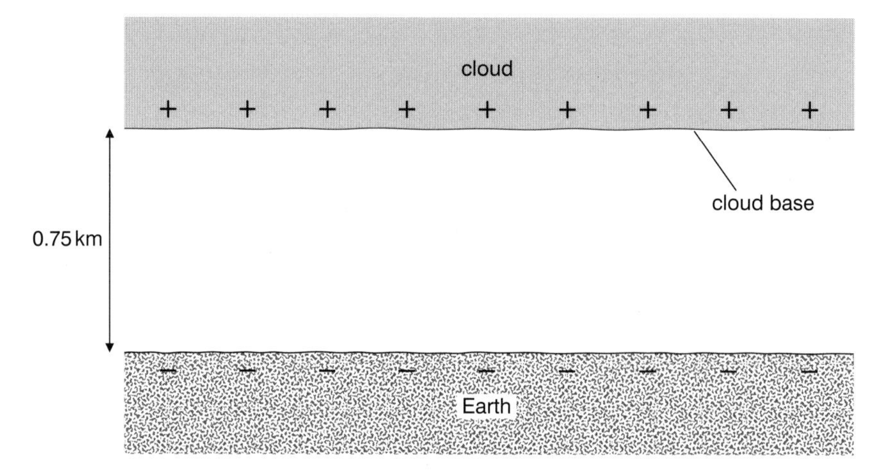

The base of the cloud and the surface of the Earth can be considered horizontal.

(i) On the diagram, sketch the electric field between the cloud and the Earth.

[3 marks]

(ii) The cloud base is 0.75 km above the Earth. A lightning flash occurs in air containing raindrops when the electric field strength exceeds $5.0 \times 10^4 \text{ N C}^{-1}$. Calculate the minimum electric potential difference between the cloud base and the Earth's surface for a lightning flash to occur.

potential difference = ... V

[2 marks]

The answers to these questions are on pages 88 and 89.

Exam question and student's answer

(a) Write down an expression for the capacitance C of a parallel plate capacitor, the plates having a common area A and being separated by a distance d, with the space between them filled by a dielectric of relative permittivity ε_r.

$$C = \frac{A\varepsilon_0\varepsilon_r}{d}$$ ✓ ✓

[2 marks]

(b) Such a capacitor has $A = 400\ \text{cm}^2$, $d = 2.00$ mm and air ($\varepsilon_r = 1.00$) as dielectric. Its plates are connected to a battery of e.m.f. 12.0 V so that it is fully charged.

(i) Calculate the energy stored in the capacitor.

$$W = \frac{1}{2}CV^2$$ ✓

$$= \frac{1}{2} \times \frac{A\varepsilon_0\varepsilon_r}{d} V^2$$ ✓

$$= \frac{\tfrac{1}{2} \times 400 \times 10^{-4} \times 8.8 \times 10^{-12} \times 1 \times 12^2}{2 \times 10^{-3}}$$

$$= 1.27 \times 10^{-8}\ \text{J}$$ ✓

[3 marks]

(ii) The capacitor is then disconnected from the battery, the charges on its plates remaining unaltered, and isolated. A sheet of glass ($\varepsilon_r = 7.5$) is inserted so that it fills the space between the plates exactly. Calculate the energy now stored in the capacitor.

$$W = 1.27 \times 10^{-8} \times 7.5$$

$$= 9.53 \times 10^{-8}\ \text{J}$$ ✗

[2 marks]

(iii) Account for the difference between your answers for **(b)(i)** and **(b)(ii)**.

glass molecules are polarized ✓ easier than air molecules so when a sheet of glass is inserted more energy is stored. ✗ ✗

[3 marks]

$[W = \frac{1}{2}QV = \frac{1}{2}CV^2]$

[Total 10 marks]

How to score full marks

Parts (a) and (b)(i)

The student's answers to these are totally correct and gain full marks as they stand. **Note that the permittivity of the medium, ε, is equal to the product of the relative permittivity, ε_r, and the permittivity of free space, ε_0, i.e. $\varepsilon = \varepsilon_r \varepsilon_0$.**

Part (b)(ii)

The student multiplied the energy stored by the relative permittivity (instead of dividing by it). Inserting a material between the plates of the capacitor does increase the capacitance but since the charge is constant it lowers the potential difference. Since the energy stored is equal to $\frac{1}{2}CV^2$ the energy is reduced by a factor of ε_r. ($C\uparrow$ by ε_r but $V^2\downarrow$ by ε_r^2 $\therefore$ overall $\downarrow$ by ε_r). The correct answer is 1.7×10^{-9} J.

The idea of polarization of the dielectric is correct and worthy of the mark gained, however it is always difficult to argue a wrong conclusion and so this is the only mark that the student scored. **As the dielectric is inserted into the capacitor each plate induces an opposite charge on the dielectric surface near it. The dielectric is therefore attracted into the capacitor and since the system does work on the dielectric the capacitor loses energy.**

Don't make these mistakes ...

If you really have no idea how to answer a calculation you are more likely to be correct if you **either multiply or divide quantities** than if you add or subtract them. When it comes to calculating quantities then do have a go – your answer (even if incorrect) may allow you to attempt later parts in the question. In the question here the student multiplied her quantities which was wrong, but **it gave her a better chance of answering the last part than no attempt would have done!**

In questions asking you to "sketch" a relationship **don't forget to include on your graph any numerical values that you know** (or can easily calculate). Be guided by the mark allocation

(1 mark – probably will not require any values, 3/4 marks – will require considerable detail).

Key points to remember

- Capacitors are devices which store charge and energy by holding opposite charges on their plates.
- $C = \frac{Q}{V}$
- C = capacitance in F; Q = charge in C; V = potential difference in V
- The farad is such a large unit that capacitors are usually quoted in microfarads (μF = F $\times 10^{-6}$) or picofarads (pF = F $\times 10^{-12}$).

- $C = \frac{\varepsilon_r \varepsilon_0 A}{d}$

where ε_0 = the permittivity of free space in F m^{-1}

ε_r = the relative permittivity of the medium between the plates (no units)

A = the area of overlap of the plates in m^2

d = separation of the plates in m

Key points to remember

- The energy stored on the capacitor = work done in taking the positive charge from the positive plate and depositing it on the negative plate.

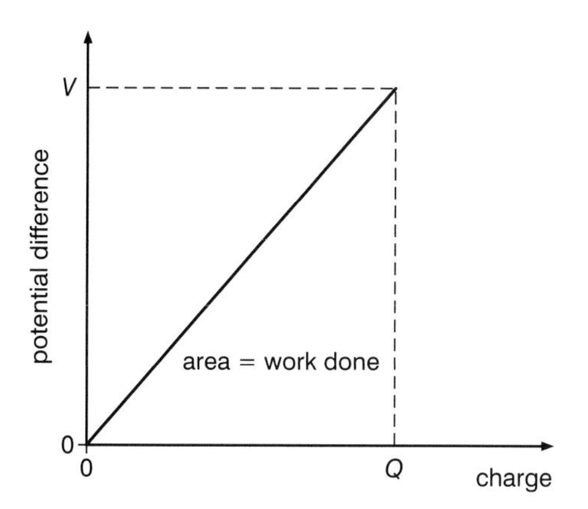

- Energy stored = area under graph

$= \frac{1}{2} QV$

$= \frac{1}{2} CV^2$

Capacitors in series

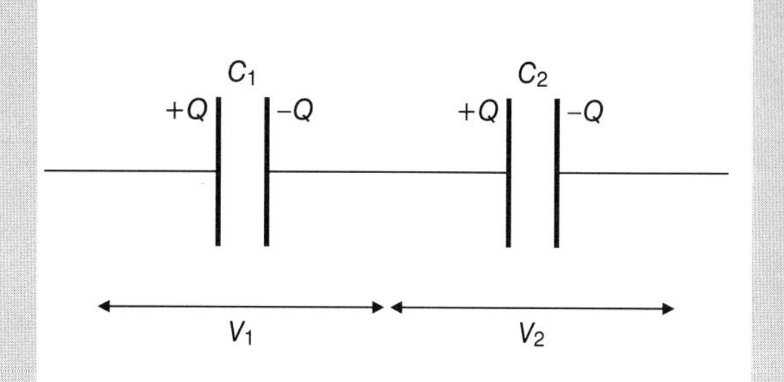

- The capacitors have equal charges on each of them.
- The total p.d. is the sum of the p.d.s across each of the capacitors.
- $\frac{1}{C} = \frac{1}{C_1} + \frac{1}{C_2}$

Capacitors in parallel

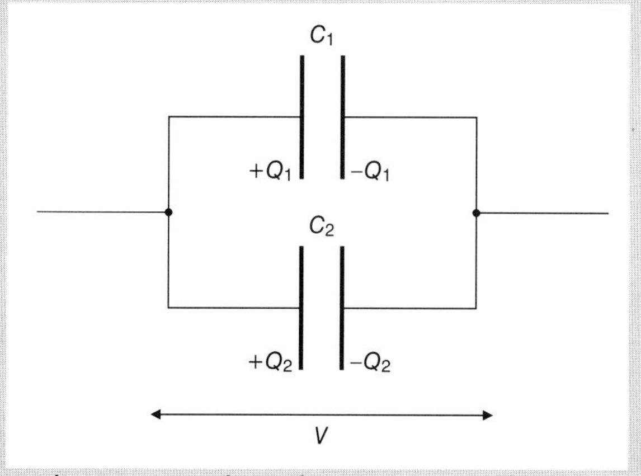

- The capacitors have the same potential difference across them.
- The total charge on the combination is the sum of the charges on the two capacitors.
- $C = C_1 + C_2$

Discharge of a charged capacitor through a resistor

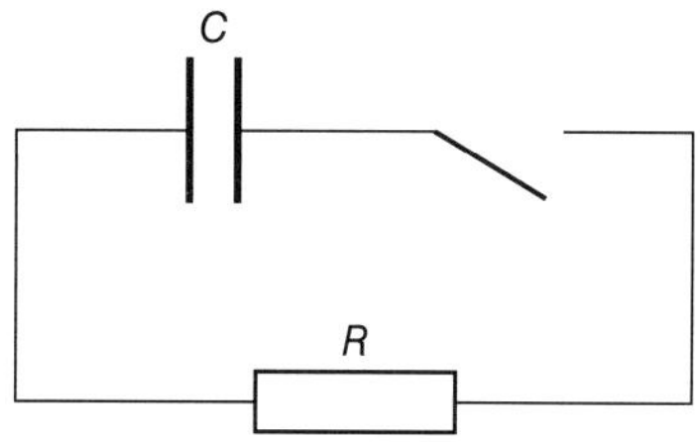

- When the switch is closed the charge passes through the resistor such that $Q = Q_0 e^{-\frac{t}{RC}}$
- Q = charge at time t, Q_0 = maximum charge (at time = 0)
- RC is called the time constant (and has units of s)
- The half-life = $0.69RC$
- This is an exponential decay.
- $\ln \frac{Q}{Q_0} = -\frac{t}{RC}$

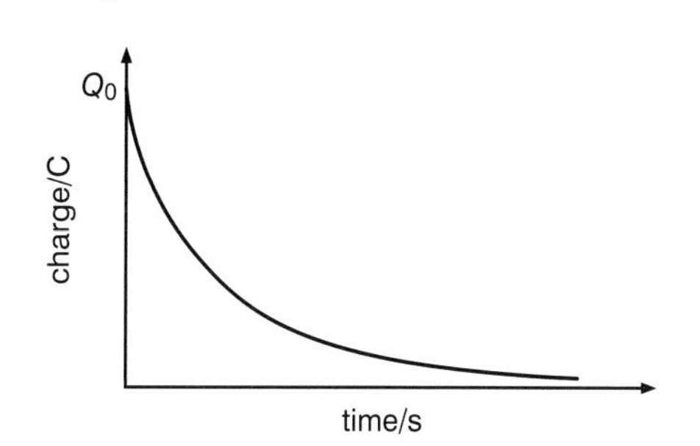

Questions to try

Examiner's hints for question 1

- **Part (a)(i):** This is not asking for a graph of the variation of charge with time. It may help to think what quantity the gradient of the graph would equal and to **look at part (ii) before answering this part**.
- **Part (b)(ii):** Since the voltage is decaying from 9.0 V to 4.5 V you can use a half-life relationship (or else you will need to take logs of the decay equation for voltage).

Q1

(a) (i) On Fig.1, sketch a graph to show the variation with charge Q of the potential difference V across a capacitor.

[2 marks]

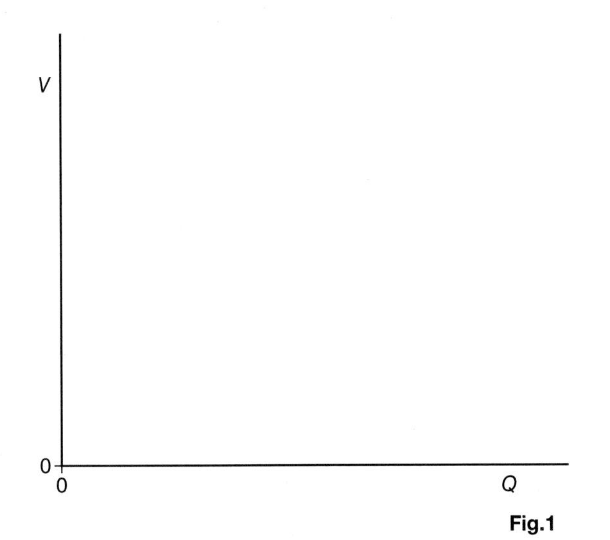

Fig.1

(i) Hence define what is meant by the *capacitance* of the conductor.

....

....

....

[2 marks]

(b) A capacitor of capacitance 5000 μF is connected in series with a resistor of resistance 12 000 Ω and a switch S, as shown in Fig.2.

Initially, the switch is open and the capacitor has a potential difference across it of 9.0 V. When S is closed, the variation with time t of the potential difference V across the capacitor is given by the expression $V = V_0 e^{-t/\tau}$.

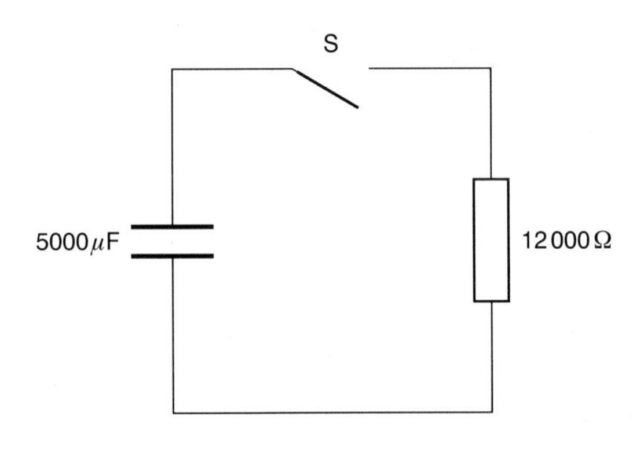

Fig 2

(i) Calculate the time constant τ.

τ = ...

[3 marks]

(ii) Calculate the time after S is closed before the potential difference across the capacitor is 4.5 V.

time = ...

[3 marks]

[Total 10 marks]

Examiner's hints for question 2

- There are similarities between this question and the previous one so no more hints here!
- You would be assessed for quality of your written communication in **part (b)(iii)** so you need to make sure that your written English is accurate and your physics is clearly explained in this part.

(a) A parallel plate capacitor is made from overlapping metal plates with an air gap in between. State two ways of increasing the capacitance of the capacitor.

....

....

[2 marks]

(b) The circuit shown below is used to provide a time delay for a burglar alarm. This time delay allows the house owner to switch off the alarm before it sounds.

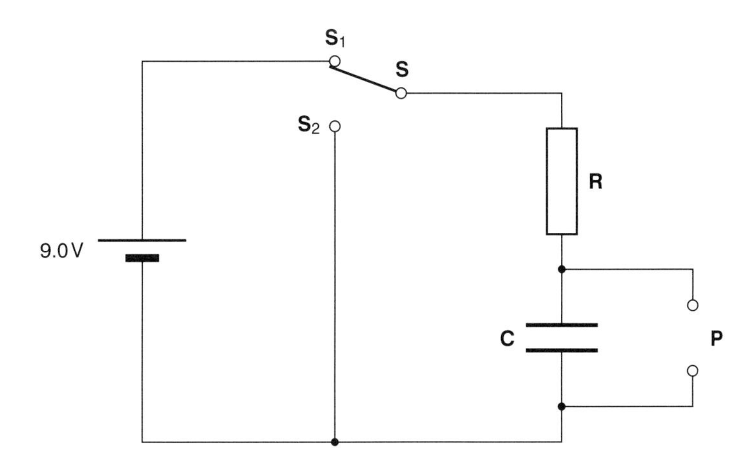

The opening of a door changes the switch **S** from position $\mathbf{S_1}$ to position $\mathbf{S_2}$. The alarm, connected to the output connections **P**, is designed to sound when the voltage across the capacitor **C** falls to 5.0 V.

(i) The capacitance of the capacitor **C** is 470 μF. The time delay between the moving of the switch to position $\mathbf{S_2}$ and the alarm sounding is 60 s.
Calculate the resistance of the resistor **R**.

[4 marks]

(ii) Sketch a graph to show the variation in voltage V across the capacitor **C** with time t, from the moment when the switch makes contact with the position $\mathbf{S}_2$.

V

t

[2 marks]

(iii) State and explain how you would modify the circuit so that the delay was 90 s instead of 60 s. You can gain up to 2 marks in this question for good written communication.

....

....

....

....

....

....

....

....

....

....

[6 marks]

[Total 14 marks]

The answers to these questions are on page 89.

Exam question and student's answer

1 The magnitude of the force on a current-carrying conductor in a magnetic field is directly proportional to the magnitude of the current in the conductor. Draw a fully labelled diagram of the apparatus you would use to verify this relationship.

State what measurements you would make and how you would use your results. You may be awarded a mark for the clarity of your answer.

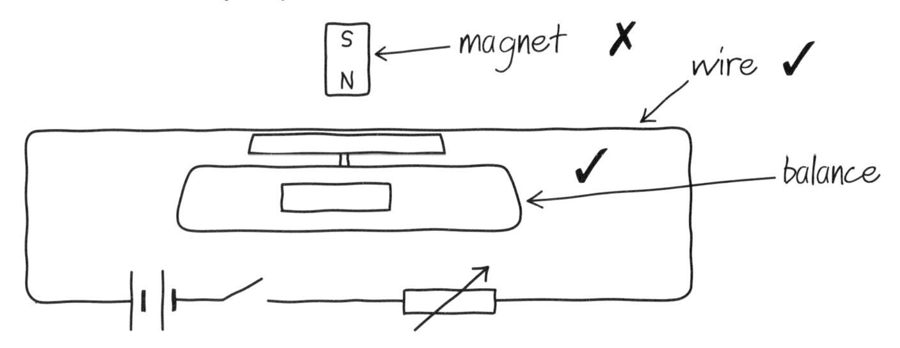

Close the switch and note the change in reading of the balance. Change the current in the wire and take new change in reading of balance. Repeat this for several current values. Plot a graph of the readings. If the results give a straight line, origin graph $F \propto I$. ✓ Q just

[6 marks]

At a certain point on the Earth's surface the horizontal component of the Earth's magnetic field is 1.8×10^{-5} T. A straight piece of conducting wire 2.0 m long, of mass 1.5 g, lies on a horizontal wooden bench in an East-West direction. When a very large current flows momentarily in the wire it is just sufficient to cause the wire to lift up off the surface of the bench.

Calculate the current.

$$F = BIl \quad \therefore \; I = \frac{F}{Bl}$$

$$= \frac{1.5 \times 10^{-3}\ \text{kg} \times 9.8\ \text{N kg}^{-1}}{1.8 \times 10^{-5}\ \text{T} \times 2.0\ \text{m}} \checkmark$$

Current = 40.8 A ✗

1/2

[2 marks]

4/8

[Total 8 marks]

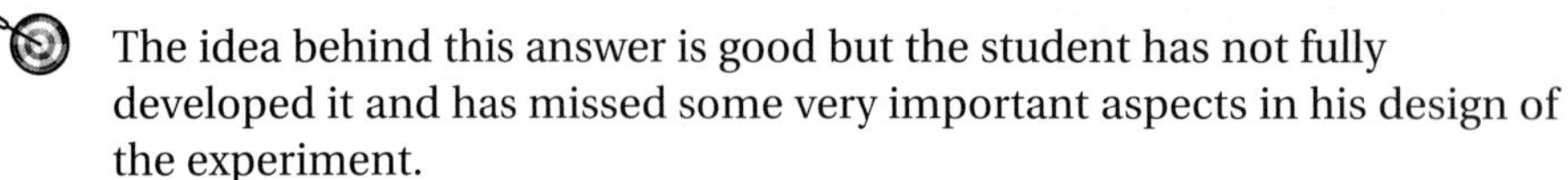

How to score full marks

- The idea behind this answer is good but the student has not fully developed it and has missed some very important aspects in his design of the experiment.
- **The magnetic field is in the wrong position** to raise the wire (as shown the wire would move into the page – applying Fleming's Left Hand rule). **The magnetic field should be directed into the page and would also need to be far more uniform** if the results were to be consistent – the bar magnet would not provide a uniform field. A pair of ceramic magnadur magnets supported on an iron yoke would be better. The student has left out his means of measuring the current – the ammeter – so he would not be able to take the readings that he mentions in his answer.
- The student talks about noting "...the change in reading of the balance". The balance is calibrated in grams and so this would need to be converted into newtons (g → kg and × 9.8 N kg^{-1} – see last part of the student's answer). This would then give values of change in the force on the wire caused by the magnetic field acting on the current-carrying wire.
- Although the student has been awarded the mark for clarity, there would be some doubt whether this mark should have been scored. **He should have said how many readings he would take and exactly what graph was being plotted.** In this case writing "F∝I" allows him to be given the benefit of the doubt as he clearly knows what is expected for the graph to show proportionality.
- A system that would have worked more effectively might be:

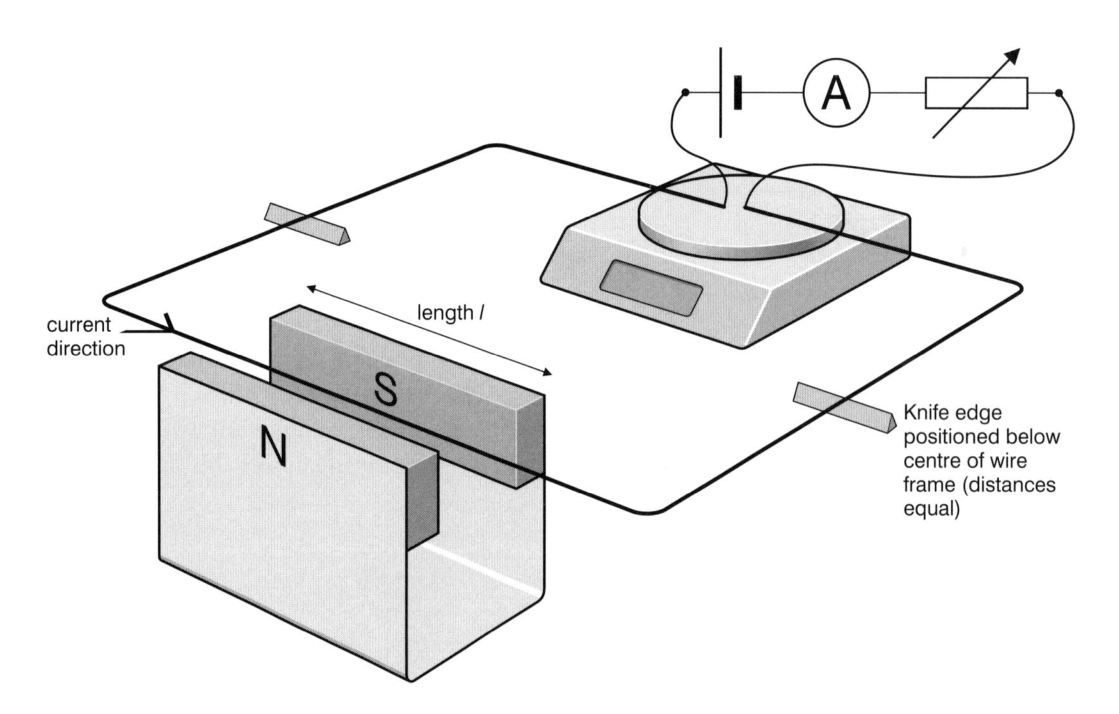

As the current is increased there will be a greater upward force on length *l* of the wire and so the force on the balance will increase. Since the frame is balanced symmetrically on the knife edges the balance registers the same "mass" change as the wire between the magnets – this must be converted into a force, of course, by multiplying the mass shown by the gravitational field strength. The length of wire inside the magnetic field is the length of the sides of the magnets and the current is that shown on the ammeter. A graph of force against current would be expected to give a straight line origin graph – indicating proportionality.

- The student's calculation is almost completely correct and very clearly laid out. However, he has made an arithmetic error and the final answer is given as 40.8 A instead of the correct 408 A. **Such slips can prove costly and he would have benefited from rechecking his calculation.**

Don't make these mistakes ...

Don't give vague answers such as "...take a few more sets of readings" or "plot a graph". **You must say how many sets of readings and what quantities you are plotting on your graph**.

Do check your calculations carefully (preferably by doing them twice). It is very easy to make numerical slips when using calculators: you should always ask yourself, "Does this answer make sense?"

Always try to **do a quick order of magnitude calculation** – in this case, the top of the calculation gives $\approx 1.5 \times 10^{-2}$; the bottom gives $\approx 4 \times 10^{-5}$; so the division gives $\approx 0.4 \times 10^{3} = 400$. So the student's answer could quickly have been seen to be the wrong order of magnitude

Key points to remember

- Electrical currents in conductors will generate magnetic fields.
- The magnetic field strength (B) will depend on the size of the current, the proximity to the conductor and the material between the conductor and the place where the field strength is being measured.
- B is also known as the magnetic flux density and is measured in units of tesla (T).
- Equations for B will be determined by the details of the conductor – whether it is a coil or a straight wire, etc. Your examination paper will provide the details of this.
- Uniform fields are those in which the lines of force are parallel and equally spaced. A current-carrying conductor placed anywhere in such a field will experience a constant force.

- A pair of parallel current-carrying wires will exert a force per unit length on each other given by

$$\frac{F}{l} = \frac{\mu_0 I_1 I_2}{2\pi a}$$

where μ_0 is the permeability of free space (its value will be given), I_1 and I_2 are the currents in the wires and a is their separation.
- This is a very important relationship in electricity since it is used to define the ampere as the S.I. base unit for electricity.
- Parallel currents will mean that the wires are attracted, and antiparallel currents mean that the wires repel each other.

- A current-carrying conductor of length l (m) at right angles to a uniform magnetic field B will experience a force F (in N) given by

$F = BIl$

where I is the current in A.
- The direction of the force can be obtained by applying Fleming's Left Hand rule – this rule applies to conventional current (the rate of flow of positive charge).
- A charge Q (in C) moving at right angles to field lines in the magnetic field will experience a force given by:

$F = BQv$

where v is the velocity of the charge (in m s^{-1}).

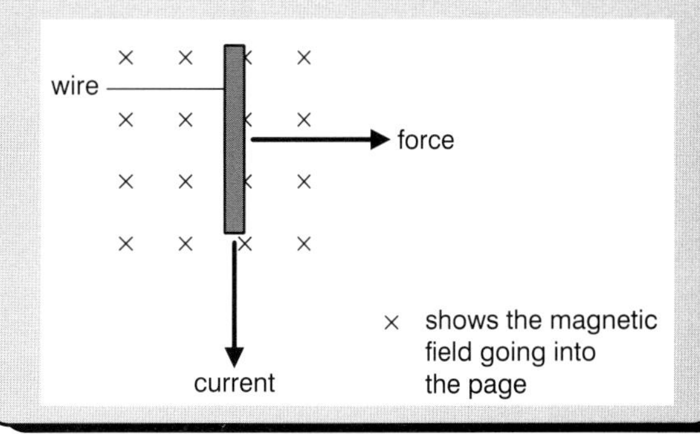

- The maximum torque on a coil of area A, having N turns and carrying a current I with its plane perpendicular to a magnetic field of strength B is given by:

$T = BIAN$

Key points to remember

Electromagnetic induction

- **Faraday's law** tells us that when a conductor cuts a magnetic field the induced emf is proportional to the rate at which the flux is being cut.
- **Lenz's law** tells us that the direction of the induced emf is so that it opposes the change that is inducing it.
- These can be summarised by the equation:

  $$E = \frac{-\Delta(N\Phi)}{\Delta t}$$

  where $\Delta(N\Phi)$ is the change in flux linkage in Wb and Δt is the time in which the flux linkage changes in seconds. The minus sign is the Lenz law contribution to the equation.

Electromagnetic induction can occur in two ways: **either** there is physical movement of the conductor such that it cuts the magnetic field **or** the magnetic field changes so that the flux linked to the conductor changes. The first of these is used with the generator and the second with the transformer.

- The generator equation is $E = E_0 \sin \omega t$ or $E = BAN\omega \sin \omega t$
  where E is the emf induced when the flux density B links with area A of the coil of N turns, ω is the angular frequency (in radians per second) and t is the time at which the emf is being measured. E_0 ($=BAN\omega$) is the maximum emf (when the plane of the coil is parallel with the flux).
- Any coil rotating in a magnetic field will experience an induced **back emf** because of electromagnetic induction.
- The transformer equation is $\frac{N_s}{N_p} = \frac{V_s}{V_p} = \frac{I_p}{I_s}$

  where the subscript 'p' denotes the primary value and 's' denotes the secondary value.
- Eddy currents are induced in a solid conductor as a result of a change of magnetic flux passing through the conductor. This wastes energy as heat is generated. Eddy currents can be reduced by increasing the resistance of the conductor by laminating it (making it out of strips of conductors joined together).

Questions to try

Examiner's hints for question 1

Part (a)

Fleming's Left Hand rule should be used with the known directions of the magnetic field and the force – to indicate the direction of the current. Once the current direction is known, this can be used with the field direction to show the directions of the forces acting on the sides of the coil.

Part (b)

The definition of a torque is = force × **perpendicular distance** from the line of action of the force to the pivot.

Q1

Fig.1 shows the front view of a pivoted square coil. The plane of the coil is at right angles to a uniform magnetic field directed into the paper. Fig.2 is a side view of the same coil.

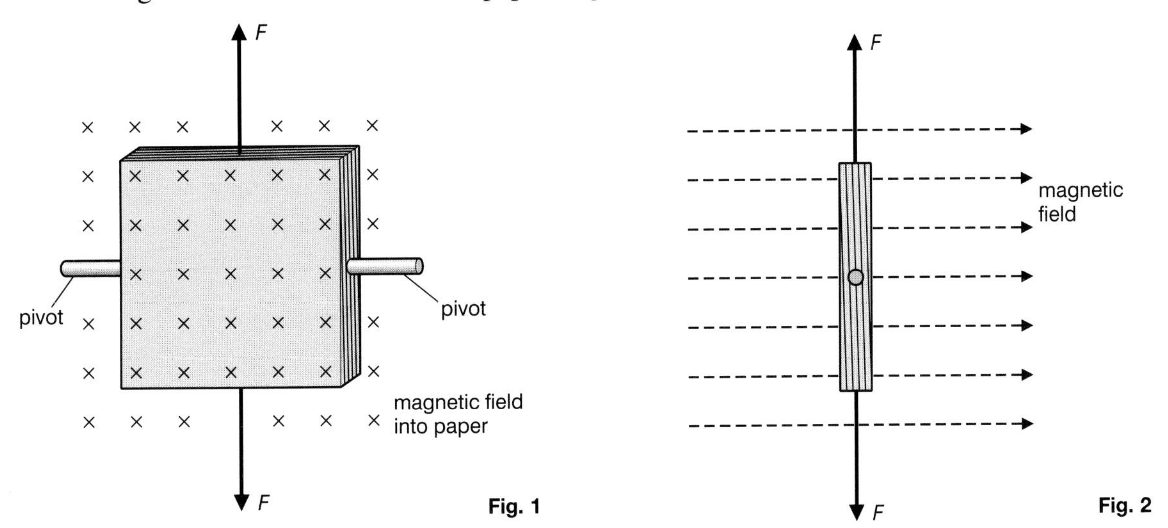

Fig. 1   Fig. 2

(a) The coil conducts a current causing electromagnetic forces to act on the coil. The directions of the forces F on the upper and lower sides are shown in both figures.

On Fig.1, draw and label arrows to show the directions of

(i) the current in the coil,

[1 mark]

(ii) the electromagnetic forces acting on the other sides of the coil.

[2 marks]

(b) Suggest why the forces in **(a)(ii)** are not considered when calculating the torque produced by the coil.

....

....

....

....

[3 marks]

[Total 6 marks]

Examiner's hints for question 2

- **Part (c)** is worth the most marks and it is completed by applying the laws of electromagnetic induction to the coil entering and leaving the field – **remember to use Lenz's law as well as Faraday's law here**.

Q2

Fig.1 shows the magnetic field between the two pole pieces of a large U-shaped magnet, with the north pole vertically above the south pole. When the strength of the magnetic field is measured along the line AB, it is found to vary as shown in Fig.2

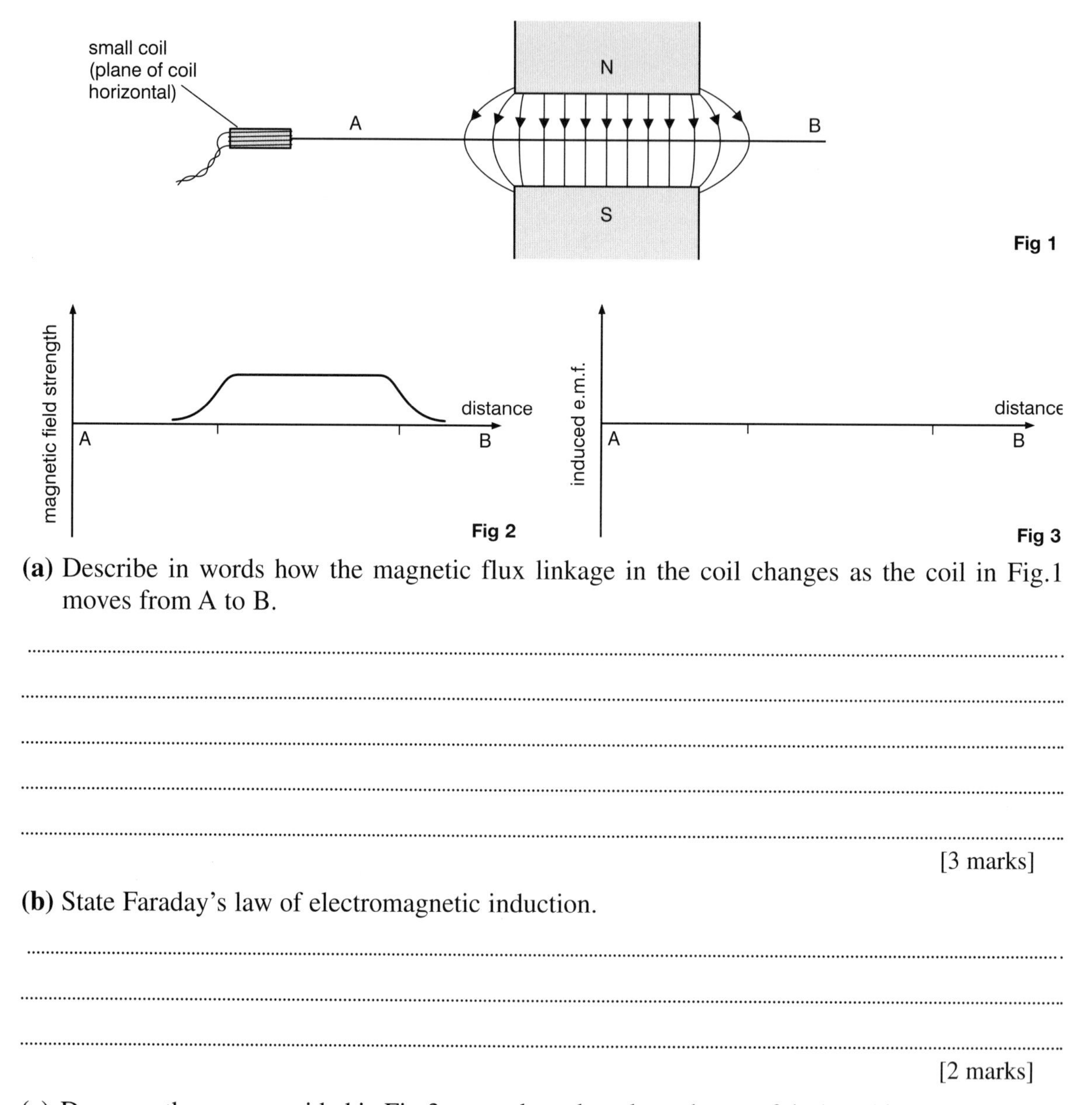

(a) Describe in words how the magnetic flux linkage in the coil changes as the coil in Fig.1 moves from A to B.

....

....

....

....

....

[3 marks]

(b) State Faraday's law of electromagnetic induction.

....

....

....

[2 marks]

(c) Draw, on the axes provided in Fig.3, a graph to show how the e.m.f. induced in the coil varies as the coil moves from A to B.

[4 marks]

[Total 9 marks]

Examiner's hints for question 3

- Don't miss out the first part of this question – it's above the diagram. You'll be expected to use the information provided in order to score all the marks.
- Transformers work using electromagnetic induction and so thinking about Faraday's law would be a good starting point for the second part of the question.
- In the third part you should write down the normal "turns ratio" equation and then think about what 100% efficient tells you about the input and output power (*P*=*IV*).

Q3

Complete the diagram below of a transformer designed to step down a potential difference of 11 kV to 415 V.

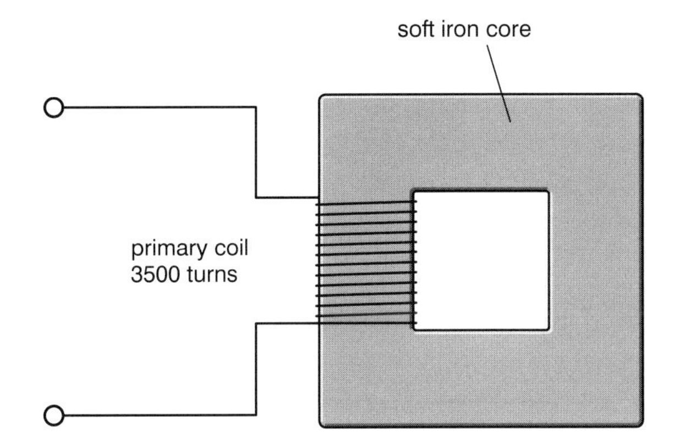

[2 marks]

Explain why the transformer could not be used to step down the potential difference of a d.c. supply.

....

....

....

[1 mark]

Show that for an ideal transformer (100% efficient)

$$\frac{I_{primary}}{I_{secondary}} = \frac{\text{Number of secondary turns}}{\text{Number of primary turns}}$$

....

....

....

....

[2 marks]

Transformers are not 100% efficient. State one cause of energy loss in a transformer.

....

....

[1 mark]

[Total 6 marks]

The answers to these questions are on page 90.

7 Radioactivity/Fission and Fusion

Exam question and student's answer

1 Nuclear power stations use nuclear fission to provide energy for electricity generation. When a nucleus of ^{235}U absorbs a neutron, it becomes unstable and undergoes fission, producing two lighter nuclei and some more neutrons. A typical reaction is

$$^{235}_{92}U + ^{1}_{0}n \rightarrow ^{141}_{56}Ba + ^{92}_{36}Kr + \text{neutrons}$$

The neutrons released can produce more fission reactions if they are captured by further ^{235}U nuclei. A reactor in a power station contains neutron-absorbing materials designed so that the chain reaction proceeds at a steady rate.

The energy released per unit mass of nuclear fuel is several orders of magnitude greater than that produced by burning chemical fuels such as oil or gas. After use, the spent fuel can be chemically treated to extract any useful materials. The remaining waste is highly radioactive.

How many neutrons are produced in the reaction above? Explain your reasoning.

Nucleon number of left hand side = 236

nucleon number of right hand side = 233 ✓

∴ r.h.s. need extra 3 ✓ neutrons to equal that of left hand side (2/2)

[2 marks]

Explain why nuclear fission releases energy.

The total mass of fission products is less ✓ than that of the original neutron + nucleus.

The difference in mass is released as kinetic energy of fission products ✓ ($E = mc^2$) (2/2)

[2 marks]

An isotope $^{235}_{92}U$ is also present within the fuel rods of a nuclear reactor. It absorbs neutrons and heavier nuclei are produced. $^{239}_{94}Pu$ (plutonium) is one of these products and particularly hazardous. $^{239}_{94}Pu$ has a half-life of 24 400 years and decays by alpha emission.

A quantity of plutonium is extracted from the fuel rods. Calculate the fraction of these $^{239}_{94}Pu$ nuclei which remain after one thousand years.

$\lambda = \frac{0.69}{T_{1/2}}$ ✓ $\therefore \frac{N}{N_0} = e^{-\lambda t} = e^{-0.69t/T_{1/2}} = e^{-0.69 \times 1000/24400}$ ✓

Fraction = 0.972 ✓

[3 marks]

Calculate the percentage decrease in the activity due to $^{239}_{94}Pu$ over this period of time.

Activity decays at the same rate as no of nuclei

Decrease in activity = 0.972

[1 mark]

In fact, if you started with a sample of pure $^{239}_{94}Pu$ the activity of the sample after one thousand years would be greater than indicated by your answer above. Suggest a reason for this.

One of decay products would decay ✓ back into $^{239}_{94}Pu$

t.o. [1 mark] 0/1

[Total 9 marks] 7/9

How to score full marks

- This is already a very good answer and the student shows that she understands the topic well by giving very clear answers to each of the first three parts. It is difficult to fault any of these answers but perhaps a more explicit link between mass conversion into kinetic energy and $E = mc^2$ could make the second part a little clearer. She could have said that **"… the difference in the mass (*m*) is released as the kinetic energy of the fission products (*E*), where *m* is related to *E* by Einstein's equation $E = mc^2$"**.
- In the fourth part of her answer the student makes the correct statement that activity and number of nuclei decay at the same rate and so she has written the percentage decrease in the activity as being that of the number of nuclei. However, her previous answer gave the fraction of nuclei *remaining* after 1000 years, **therefore the fraction decayed was 0.028 (≈ 3%)** – this is the correct answer to the fourth part.
- Having actually answered the fifth part nearly completely correctly by saying that one of the decay products would decay, the student then talks herself out of the mark by saying that it would return to the original isotope (which it could not do by natural means). All she needed to say was **that the products of the decay of plutonium may, themselves, be radioactive and contribute to the overall activity of the sample.**

Don't make these mistakes…

Don't think that you know what a question says without really reading it through completely. The more competent you become at answering questions, the more confident you become too. This is good! **But don't become over-confident**, as the student was in answering the fourth part of this question. If she had read the question clearly and thought about it, she could have answered this part correctly.

Do show all the relevant equations, as this student has done in answering the third part – if her calculation had been wrong she would still have picked up one or two of the three marks by showing her equations and substitution of values very clearly.

Key points to remember

Nuclear stability

- The ratio of the number of neutrons to the number of protons determines whether or not a nucleus is stable or unstable (radioactive).
- For lighter elements isotopes with approximately equal numbers of protons and neutrons are stable.
- More massive stable isotopes will lie in the shaded region of the chart of neutron number (N) against proton number (Z).

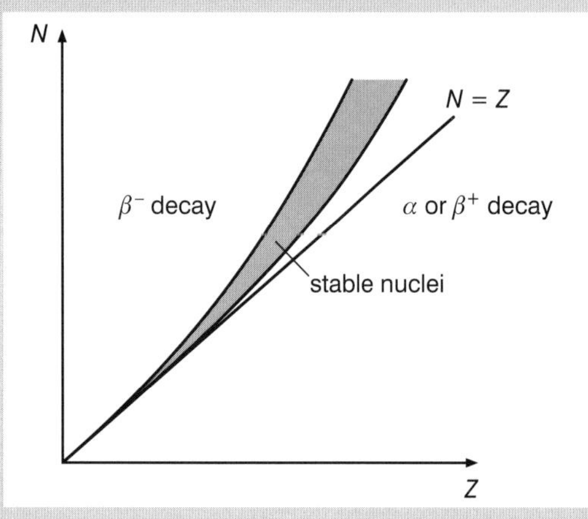

- Above the curve β^- decay occurs (increasing Z and decreasing N).
- Below the curve α (for high Z) or β^+ decay occurs (each increasing N and decreasing Z).
- Each decay brings the daughter nuclide closer to the region of stability.

The decay equation

- The rate of decay of a nuclide is proportional to the number of radioactive nuclei present:
- $\frac{dN}{dt} \propto N$ or $\frac{dN}{dt} = \lambda N$

  This equation leads to the relationship $N = N_0 e^{-\lambda t}$ where λ is the decay constant in units of s^{-1}, min^{-1}, etc.
- This is very similar to capacitor discharge and similar techniques may be used in explanations, calculations and graphs.
- The half-life $T_{1/2} = \frac{0.69}{\lambda}$

See *Do Brilliantly AS Physics* (p.69) for further details of radioactive decay.

Fission and fusion

- Einstein's equation $E = mc^2$ shows the equivalence of mass and energy. E is the energy equivalence of mass m and c is the speed of electromagnetic waves in a vacuum.
- When the mass of a nucleus is compared with the total mass of its constituent particles there is found to be less mass in the nucleus – this difference is known as the **mass defect**.
- Using Einstein's relationship the mass defect has an energy equivalence which is known as the **nuclear binding energy**.
- The nuclear binding energy can also be thought of as the energy that needs to be supplied in order to separate the nucleons within the nucleus.
- In order to compare different nuclei it is important to consider **the nuclear binding energy per nucleon** – this is different for different nuclei. Nuclear binding energy is the idea which explains nuclear fission and nuclear fusion.
- The nuclear binding energy per nucleon is **least for the very light elements** like hydrogen. When two light nuclei are fused (at very high temperature) the binding energy per nucleon of the resultant nucleus is increased and the difference is released as energy.
- The nuclear binding energy is also **lower for the massive elements** like uranium **than for the less massive ones** like iron. When a uranium nucleus is caused to split into two lighter nuclei the binding energy per nucleon increases and energy is released (due to the increased nuclear binding energy).

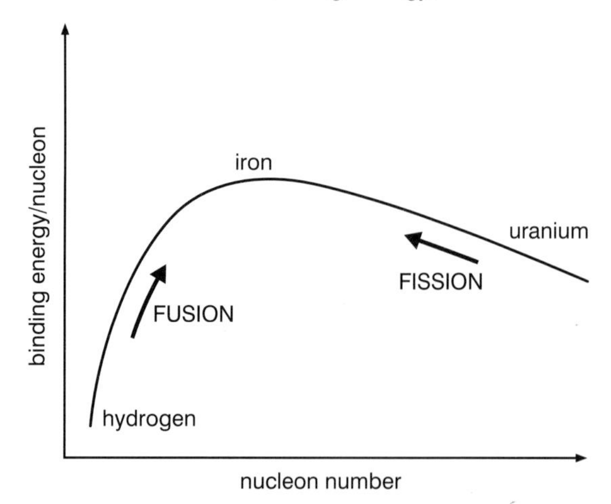

Questions to try

Examiner's hints for question 1

- The 'Key points to remember' section covers **parts (a)** and **(b)**.
- **Part (c)** R represents the radius of the atom in this question. You will need to think about the definition of density and the relationship between the volume of a sphere and its radius. This is quite tricky and you will need to realise that the nucleon number is proportional to the mass of an atom.

Q1

(a)(i) Sketch a graph to show how the neutron number, N, varies with the proton number, Z, for naturally occurring stable nuclei over the range $Z = 0$ to $Z = 90$. Show values of N and Z on the axes of your graph and draw the $N = Z$ line.

N

Z

(ii) On your graph mark points, one for each, to indicate the position of an unstable nuclide which would be likely to be

an α emitter, labelling it A,

a β^- emitter, labelling it B.

[5 marks]

(b) State the changes in N and Z which are produced in the emission of

(i) an α particle,

....

....

(ii) a β^- particle.

....

....

[2 marks]

(c) The results of electron scattering experiments using different target elements show that

$R = r_0 A^{1/3}$

where A is the nucleon number and r_0 is a constant.

Use this equation to show that the density of a nucleus is independent of its mass.

....

....

....

....

[3 marks]

[Total 10 marks]

Examiner's hints for question 2

Part (a)

You could probably write a long essay on this question but it's only worth a mark so you should concentrate on what is fundamental about radioactive decay – remember that it occurs in the nucleus of a nuclide.

Part (b)

(i) **(I)** For a single mark you will only be expected to calculate the half-life once – but do mark it on the graph.

(II) Start off by writing down the relationship between decay constant and half-life.

(ii) **(I)** Don't spend too long on this – it's only worth 2 marks and so there should be quite generous tolerance allowed for answers.

(II) As always, multiplying the units of the quantities along the x and y-axes will give the units of the quantity represented by the area.

No hint for the last part!

Q2

(a) Explain what is meant by *radioactive decay*. [1 mark]

....

....

....

....

....

(b) The radioactive isotope ${}^{b}_{a}X$ is known to emit alpha and gamma radiations in decaying to the atom Y. The activity of a sample of ${}^{b}_{a}X$ was measured over a period time and a graph of the results obtained is shown below.

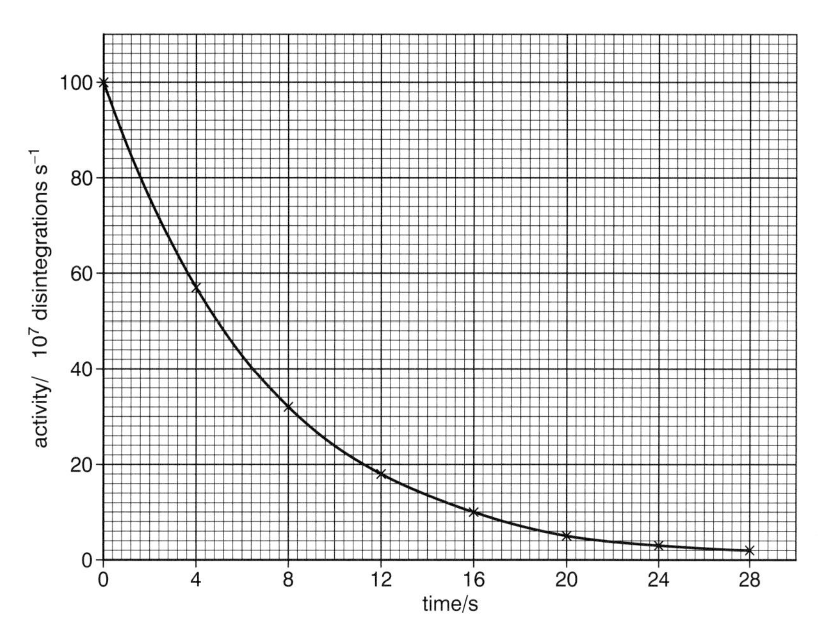

(i) (I) Find the half-life.

....

[1 mark]

(II) Hence calculate the decay constant of ${}^{b}_{a}X$.

....

....

....

[3 marks]

(ii) (I) Find the area under the graph line from $t = 0$ to $t = 4$ s.

....

....

[2 marks]

(II) What does this area represent?

....

[1 mark]

Write down an equation to show the decay of ${}^{b}_{a}X$ to Y.

....

....

[2 marks]

[Total 10 marks]

The answers to these questions are on page 91.

8 How to Revise for Synoptic Questions

What are synoptic questions?

Each of the GCE Awarding Bodies must include a paper, or papers, which are called "synoptic". **Synoptic questions are those that bring together ideas, knowledge and skills that you have developed throughout the course** and require you to be able to make links between the different things that you have studied. Synoptic papers must be sat at the very end of the course and are worth 20% of the whole A level.

As far as you are concerned, these papers mean that **you have to revise all the work that you have covered over the whole of the course.** This may sound daunting but you must remember that you have learned a lot as you have progressed through your 'AS' and 'A2' studies and so it is not at all like starting from scratch!

You may find that one or more of your modules is an option and, since not everybody studies the same options, you cannot possibly be examined on this directly.

Although each of the GCE Awarding Bodies has approached synoptic assessment in slightly different ways, there are many **common themes** that run through.

Since you, as an examination candidate, **are required to make links in your learned knowledge and understanding,** the examiners cannot structure questions in the same way as they do in other examination papers. This means that they must stimulate you into thinking about chosen topics and hope that you can make the mental jumps that are required to answer the questions in an appropriate way.

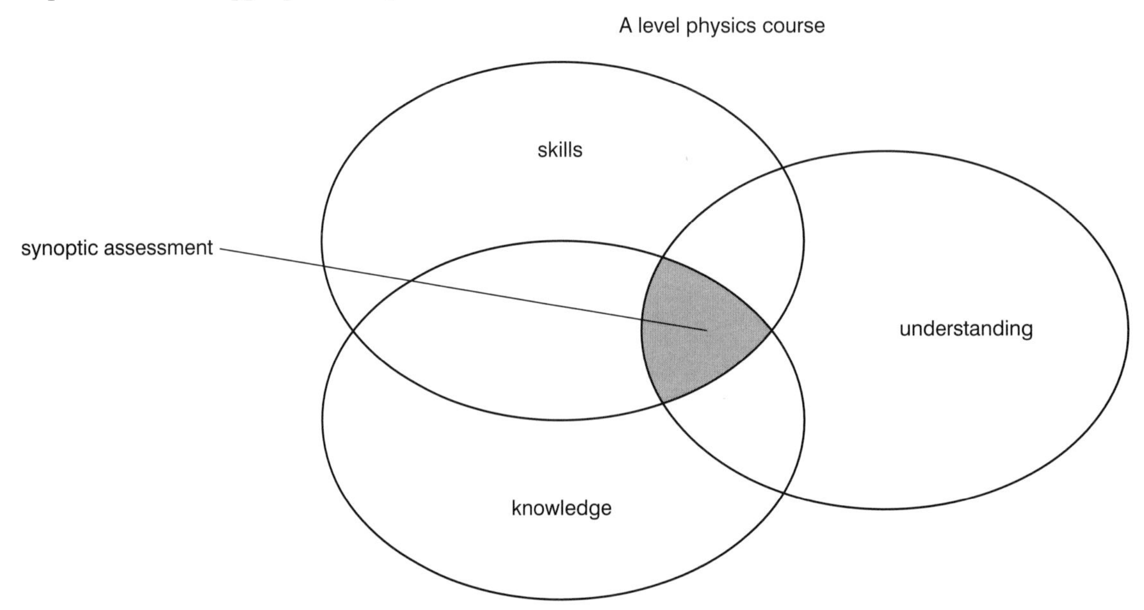

Typical tasks and stimuli will be:

- **Comprehension of a passage** based on scientific or technological information.
- **Calculations and deductions** from graphical or tabular information.
- **Structured questions** that may require you to answer parts from a whole series of topics from anywhere within your specification.

Mind maps or spidergrams

It is extremely valuable to **look at the links that crop up in different topics.** For example: circular motion is a topic that we looked at in chapter 1. Ideas relating to circular motion also crop up in gravitation, electrostatics, magnetic fields and particle accelerators:

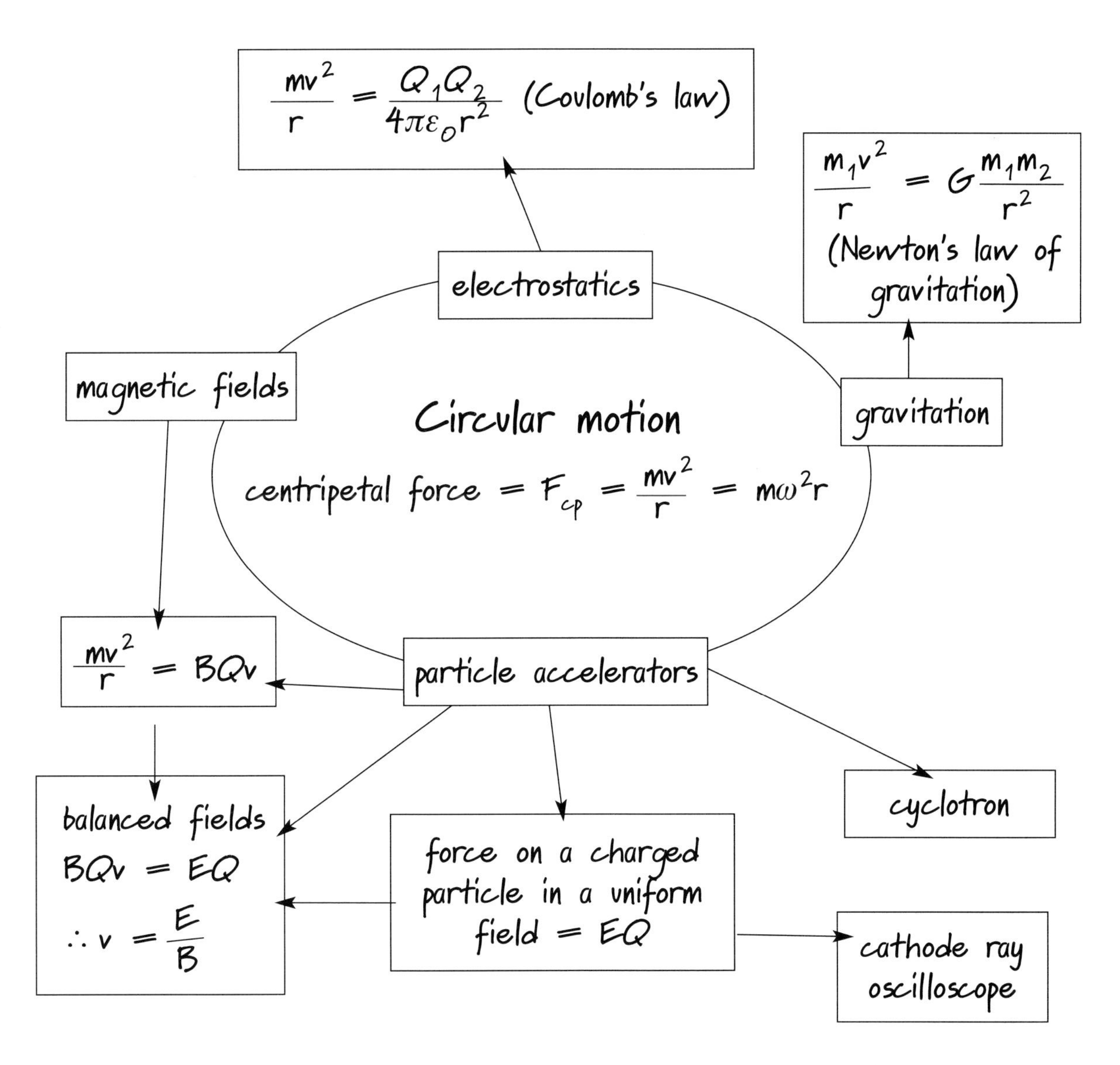

I've concentrated on the equations in this spidergram but you may also be able to think of non-equation links appropriate to the specification that you have studied. **It is equally valid to do the same sort of thing with written ideas,** such as the range of waves making up the electromagnetic spectrum – their uses and how each of the waves can be used. Spidergrams can be a productive way to revise for an exam, particularly if the emphasis of the course is on understanding and applying abstract, theoretical material, rather than on simply reproducing memorised information. **Doing a spidergram of your course content can point out the most important concepts and principles and allow you to see the ways in which they fit together.** Since your spidergram may have missing details, drawing a spidergram could also help you to **focus on your weaknesses too!**

It is important to interact with others if you can and so it can be very helpful to draw spidergrams with friends. In this way you can each see what others consider to be the important aspects of a topic, and also links that you have not thought of.

Flow diagrams

These are a very useful way of **visualising sequential aspects of your specification**. Again they can let you see links clearly and can summarise much in a relatively small space. As with spidergrams, don't think that you will produce a perfect flow diagram first time: **you may need a couple of drafts to get it right**. Flow diagrams are particularly useful for **describing experimental techniques**. For example, in electromagnetic induction you may be asked how you would investigate how the emf induced in one coil depends upon the frequency of the alternating current in a second coil:

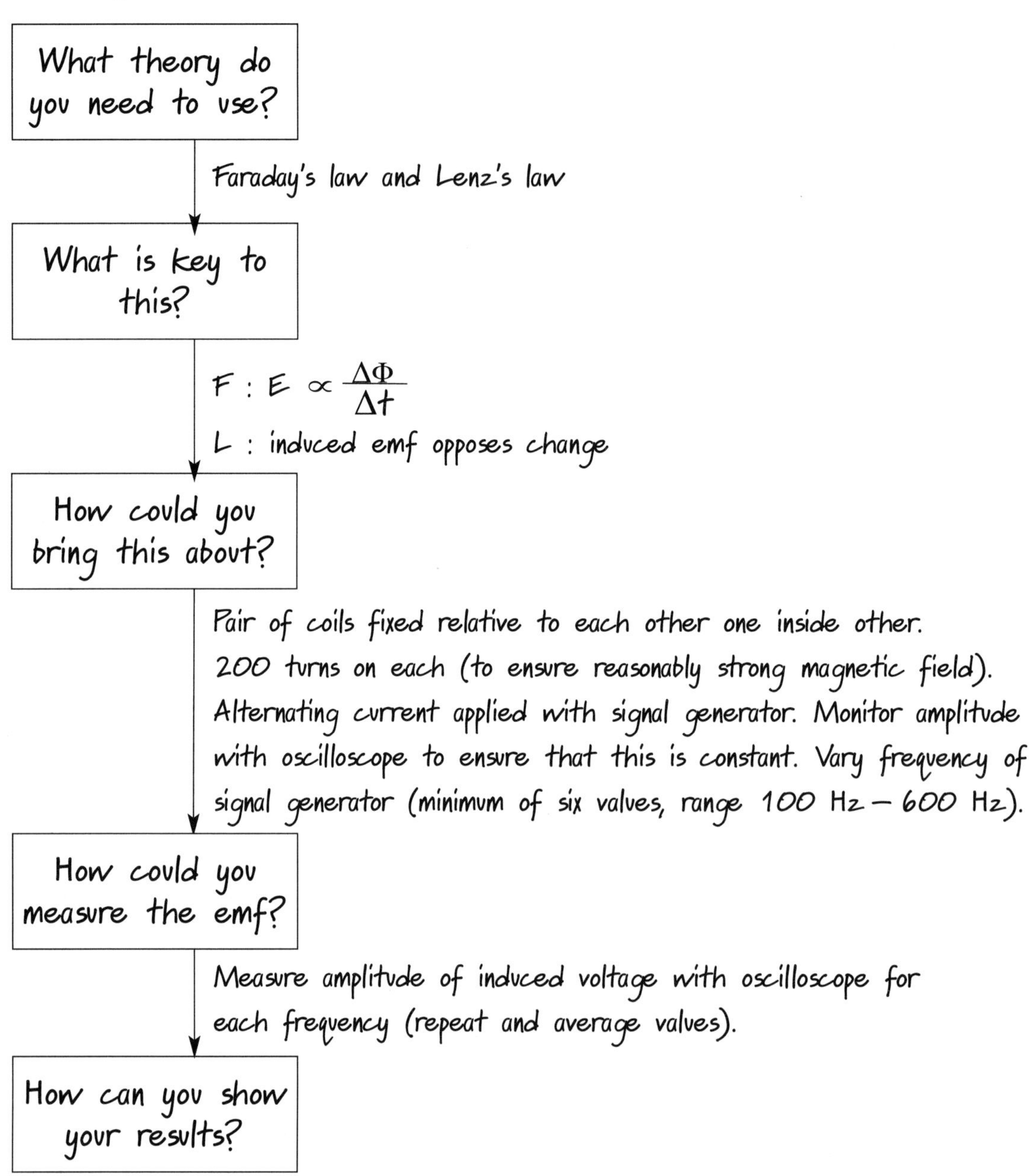

Whether or not this answer is sufficiently complete would depend on the context of the question being asked. You could make it even more appealing and personalised by **including diagrams**. The diagram provides a structure that can be generalised to pretty much any experiment or demonstration.

Sets (Venn diagrams)

When you are thinking about the links between different topics it is useful to **consider the similarities and differences between those topics**. For example, gravitation and electrostatics offer an ideal opportunity to make such a comparison (as does the flow of charge, the flow of thermal energy and the flow of matter). This is quite a nice way of focusing on the similarities and differences between topics and offers an alternative to the more usual split list.

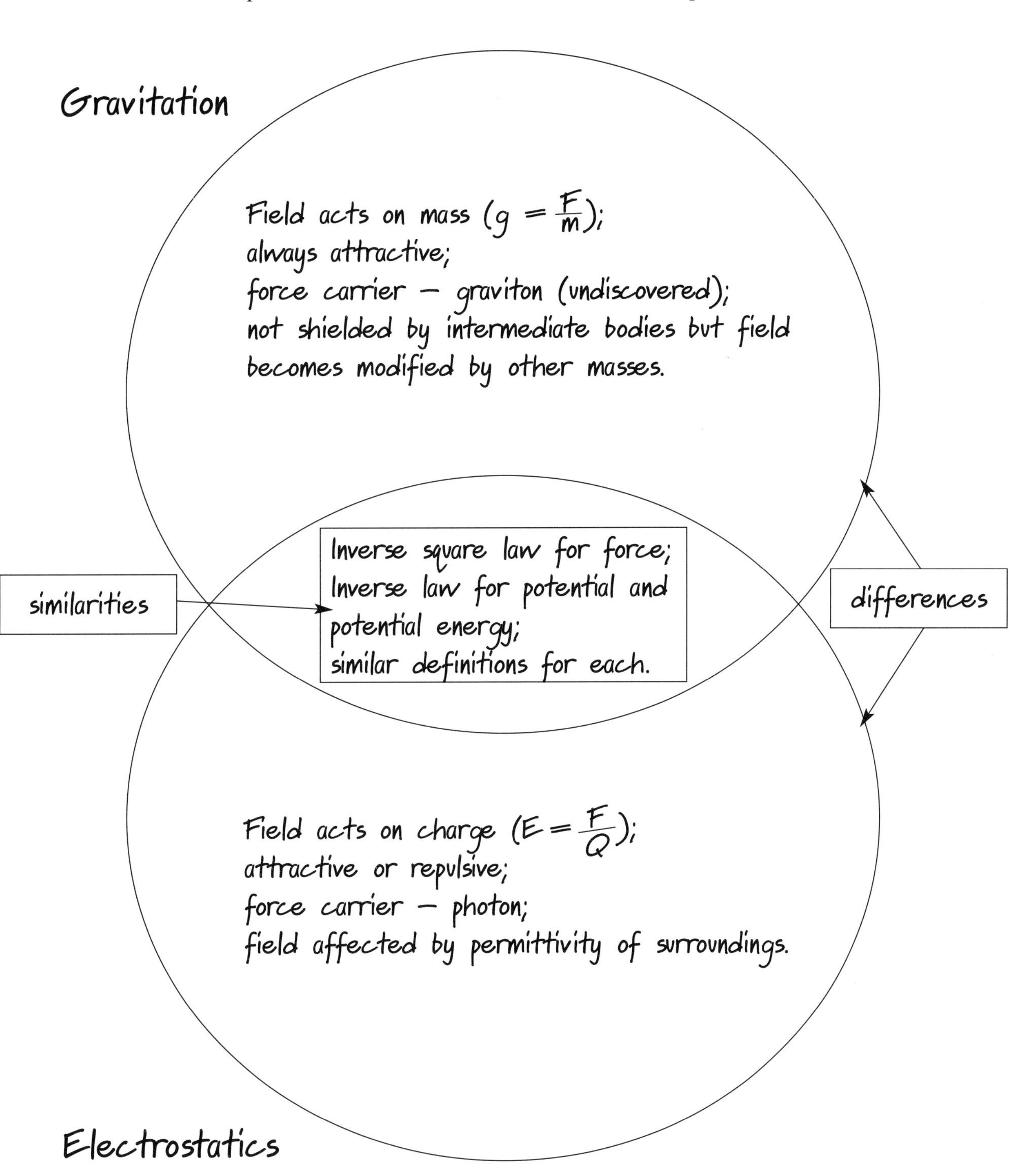

Tree Chart

This is another method of linking topics. Starting with a common theme, **the topic is broken down section by section** until you are happy or can go no further! Let's look at exponential decays.

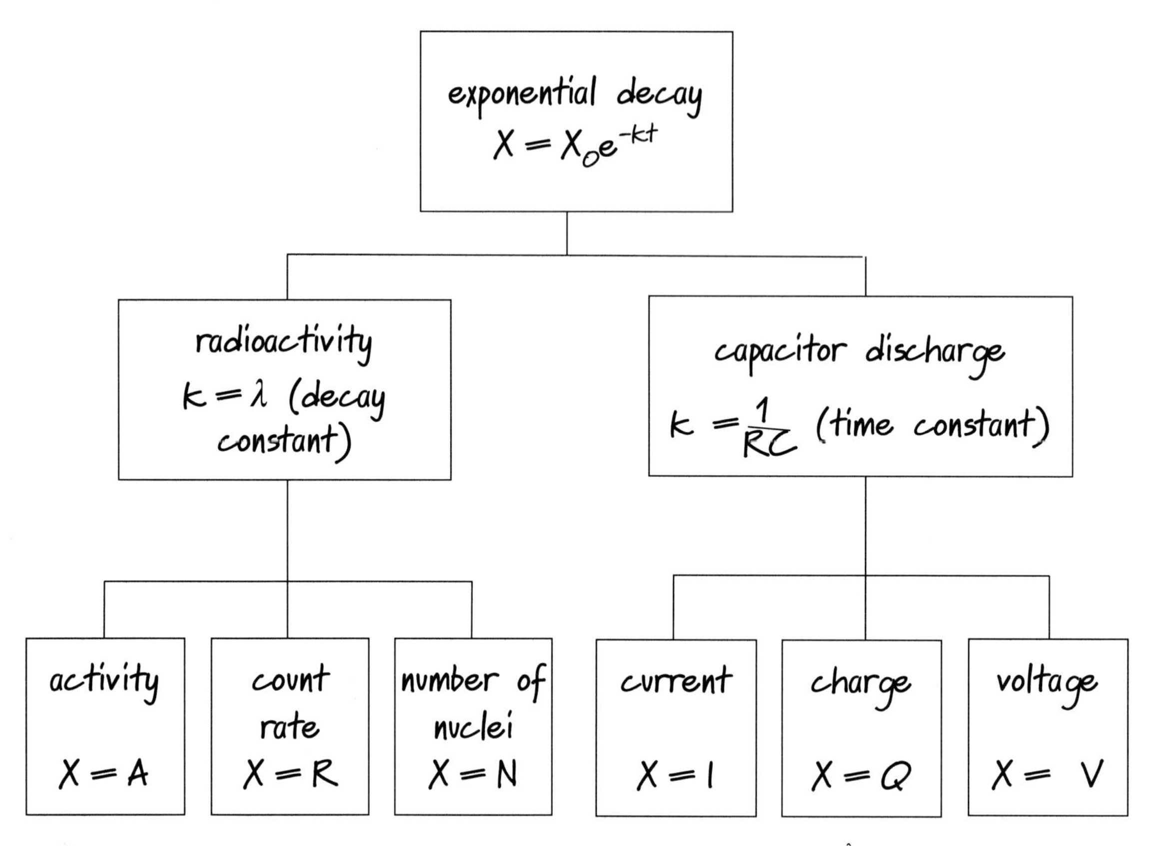

This indicates how many equations come from the same route! $A = A_0e^{-\lambda t}$, etc. Each of these takes the same general shape:

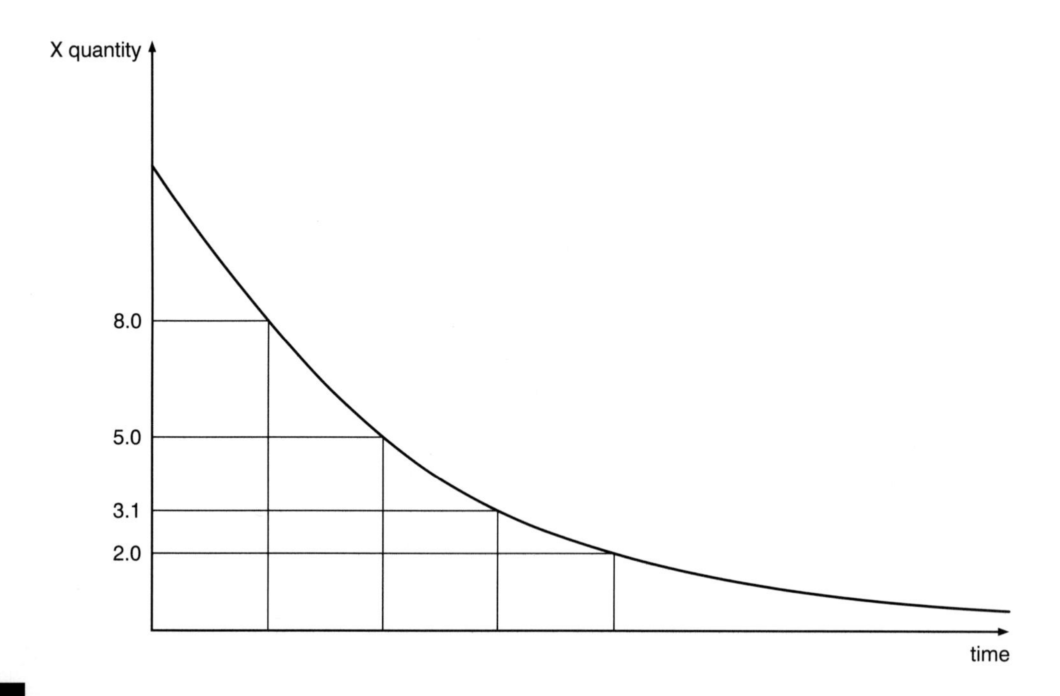

Properties of these curves are that they have a constant “half-life” or there is a constant ratio of “y” values for equal “t” values.

e.g. $8.0:5.0 \simeq 5.0:3.1 \simeq 3.1:2.0$

You should also think about what happens when the constant k is made larger or smaller. When k is larger, it means that the decay happens faster therefore the gradient becomes steeper – this is the effect of having a larger λ or a smaller RC product.

The next three chapters (chapters 9–11) contain examples of the different ways in which the exam boards test your physics synoptically:

- **Comprehension questions** – a short scientific article and then a series of questions that are focused on the physics that relates to the article – see chapter 9.
- **Data analysis questions** – data provided in a table or on a graph and then questions which relate the topic area with numerical parts that make use of the data provided – see chapter 10.
- **Structured questions** – usually taken from a wide range of topics that may or may not be linked together. These questions will usually cover material from many different units in your specification – see chapter 11.

Wind Power Generation

The power available to a wind turbine depends on the kinetic energy of a column of air with the same cross-sectional area A as the wind turbine rotor blades.

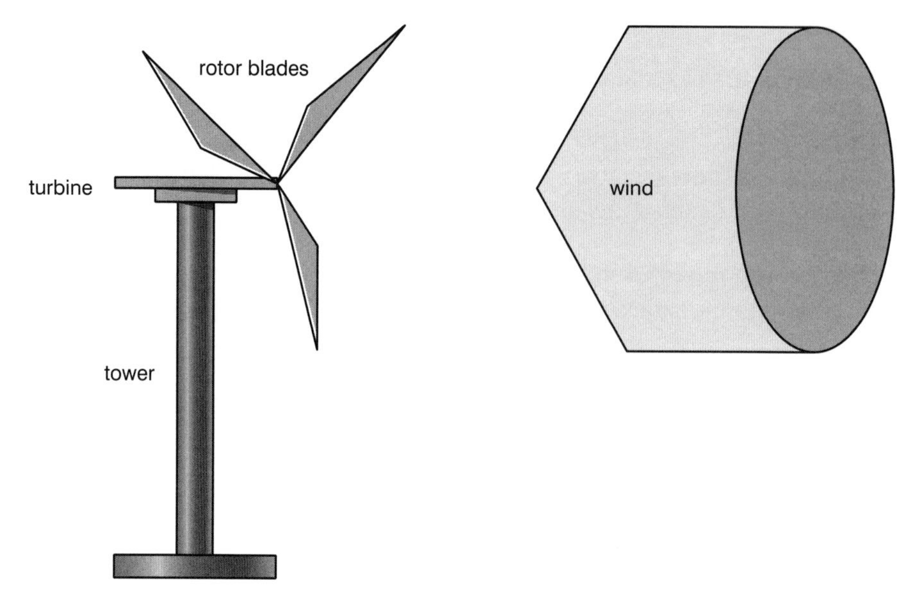

The available power P in the wind is given by $P = \frac{1}{2}\rho A u^3$

where ρ is the density of the air, u is the wind speed.

A steady supply of reasonably strong wind is necessary for utilising the power in the wind. Modern wind turbines are designed to operate most efficiently when the wind speeds are within the range 10 m s^{-1} to 15 m s^{-1}. At a wind speed of 10 m s^{-1} one wind turbine can supply the National Grid with about 4 A at a transformed voltage of 100 000 V.

Many wind turbines are designed to be stationary when u is below 5 m s^{-1}. The rate of rotation reaches a maximum when u is about 12 m s^{-1} and cuts out, for safety reasons, when u is above 25 m s^{-1}.

There are structural problems to overcome. For example, a 50 m tall wind turbine tower will swing back and forth slightly. If a rotor blade passed the tower each time the tower was in one of its extreme positions, then the oscillations might become large enough to cause structural damage.

There is a European Union-wide target to provide 12% of the electricity requirements from renewable energy sources by the year 2010. In the UK approximately half of this could be feasibly supplied by wind power. "However, current policies are not likely to deliver this". (Lords' report on Electricity from Renewables – June 99.)

(a) Calculate the efficiency of conversion σ of wind power to electrical power when the wind speed is 10 m s^{-1}. Use the data given in paragraph 1 and take the density of air to be 1.2 kg m^{-3} and the diameter of a rotor blade to be 44 m. State any assumptions made.

$P = \frac{1}{2}\rho A u^3$

$P = \frac{1}{2} \times 1.2 \times \frac{44^2}{4}$ ✓✓ $\pi \times 10^3$

$= 9.12 \times 10^5$ W (3sf) ✓

$P = IV$ ✓

$= 4 \times 100\ 000$

$= 4 \times 10^5$ W ✓

$\frac{4 \times 10^5}{9.12 \times 10^5} \times 100\% = 43.8\%$ (3sf) ✓

assuming density to be constant ∧

[7 marks]

(b) By considering the volume of air which passes through a cross-sectional area *A* in one second, show that the power available is given by

$$P = \tfrac{1}{2}\rho A u^3$$

volume of air passing cross-section per second:

$V/t = Au$ ✓

$Au\rho = \frac{m}{t}$ ✓

$Au^3\rho = \frac{mu^2}{t}$

$Au^3\rho = mau$

$Au^3\rho = Fu$

$P = \frac{1}{2}Au^3\rho$

2/4

[4 marks]

(c) Explain why it is *impossible* for all the kinetic energy available in the wind to be transferred to the kinetic energy of the rotor blades.

Energy is lost in overcoming friction in various moving parts such as the blades' axle, thus the k.e. would be lost as heat energy – there are no perfect frictionless moving parts. ✗

0/2

[2 marks]

(d) State three conditions, other than change in wind speed, which may reduce the power output of this system.

Reduce the density of the air by high altitude, ✓ shorter blades so smaller cross-sectional area A. ✓ Direction of the wind, if it blows from sideways positions, it causes fewer rotations at lower speed. ✓

3/4

[4 marks]

(e) Assuming the period of oscillation of the turbine tower is 3.0 s, calculate the angular velocity of the rotor which would be dangerous.

The blade passing the tower each time it is in one of its extreme positions means that they have the same period.

$\frac{2\pi}{T} = \omega$ ✓

$\omega = 2.09$ rad s^{-1} ✓ ✓

3/3

[3 marks]

(f) Explain why the oscillations referred to in paragraph four of the passage can become very large in certain circumstances.

When the wind blows so that the tower is oscillating at its resonance frequency ✓ and the blade has the same period ^ then oscillations can be large.

[2 marks]

(g) Why is it desirable to increase the percentage of the electricity requirements provided by renewable energy? Give one problem in increasing the production of electricity from wind power.

Non-renewable energy source is depleting quickly and may not be able to supply energy demands in the future. ✓ A large number of windmills are needed to supply large amounts of energy. These would take up a large area of land, ✓ also there would be some ^ pollution and there could be difficulty in selecting a location with appropriate wind speed.

2/2

[2 marks]
[Total 24 marks]

How to score full marks

Part (a)

This part is well answered and gains a high mark. You should try to give more explanation of what is going on in the calculation than this student has done (such as saying that $P = IV$, corresponding to the electrical power output). The calculation is correct but the assumption that the density [of the air] is constant is too trivial to score a mark. **The examiners expected the student to explain that the electrical power calculation is only correct if we assume that the generator used is 100% efficient.**

Part (b)

The first two lines of this proof are valid **(the rate of flow of volume = area × velocity and volume flow rate is converted to mass flow rate by multiplying by the density)**. The next three lines are mathematically correct (if we assume that the velocity falls from value u to 0 in time t). This working is indicative of a student who doesn't really know what he is doing!

A better approach would be:

power = rate of change of kinetic energy of wind
power = $\Delta(^1/_2 mu^2)/t$

rate of flow of volume = Au
rate of flow of mass = ρAu
power = $\Delta(^1/_2 \rho Auu^2)$
power = $^1/_2 \rho Au^3$ (when the velocity falls to zero in time t)

Part (c)

Although friction is a good fall back answer, the correct one is more fundamental to the flow of gases. **If the air lost all of its kinetic energy it would stop moving and there would be nowhere for the next layer of air to go. So the wind turbine would stop turning.**

Part (d)

These are sensible suggestions and gain marks. The "direction of the wind" could have been better phrased by saying **that if the wind is not normal to the blades only the component of the wind velocity that is normal will be effective.**

Other suggestions might be:
- Turbulent wind flow.
- Friction in the bearings of the rotor.

NB it is unusual to offer four marks for three conditions so it is likely that one of the expected answers needs a little explanation (such as the student's third point).

Part (e)

This part is well answered and gains full marks.

Part (f)

Just a couple of things would make this answer completely correct:
- Resonance would occur when **the frequency of the rotor matched the natural frequency of the tower.**
- The **amplitude** of the oscillations would become large.

Part (g)

These are perfectly good answers to this standard question. An advantage of wind farms is that they **do not pollute the environment** and so the student nearly talked himself out of a mark – he should have said that wind turbines may produce **noise** pollution.
Other disadvantages of wind generators are:
- **Their power output is relatively low.**
- **They are unreliable if the wind drops (hinted at in the student's answer).**
- **A large area of land is needed for a wind farm.**

Don't make these mistakes ...

Don't forget to **read the passage through before you start to answer** comprehension questions! You are likely to be in such a rush to write your answers down that you read the passage through quickly or not at all. You must read it because **it sets the context for the questions that follow**.

Do use a highlighter to **highlight important data** in the passage. It will allow you to return to it quickly.

Don't think comprehension questions are purely descriptive. Examiners will expect you to use the data in the passage to answer the questions. Whenever you can **support your arguments with data or calculations** you should do so, but do not spend too long doing this.

Pace yourself throughout your answer and work out how long you can afford to spend on the question by the formula:

$$\textbf{minutes on question} = \frac{\textbf{number of marks on question} \times \textbf{length of exam in minutes}}{\textbf{total number of marks on paper}}$$

Questions to try

The total time of the exam, from which these questions are taken, was 120 minutes and there was a total of 100 marks for it. You should spend about 30 minutes on your answers to all three questions.

Mineral prospecting

Exploration for new ore deposits by drilling holes in the Earth can be a costly hit and miss exercise. The geophysicist employs physics to search for the location of ore deposits. The techniques used come from almost all branches of physics. Optical and infrared satellite photographs are first used to identify likely areas for further tests. Experiments are then carried out to investigate variations in one or usually several physical factors. For example, ores may produce local variations in the strength of the Earth's magnetic field, in the strength of the Earth's gravitational attraction, in the electrical resistivity of the Earth, in the speed of waves through the Earth (seismology) or, for radioactive ores, in the count rate measured using a radiation detector.

Voltage measurements to detect variation in resistivity

These measurements use the principle of the potential divider. Two methods are commonly used. In the method shown in **Figure 1**, a battery is connected to two electrodes **A** and **B** which are inserted in the ground some distance apart, ensuring good electrical contact between the electrodes and the soil.

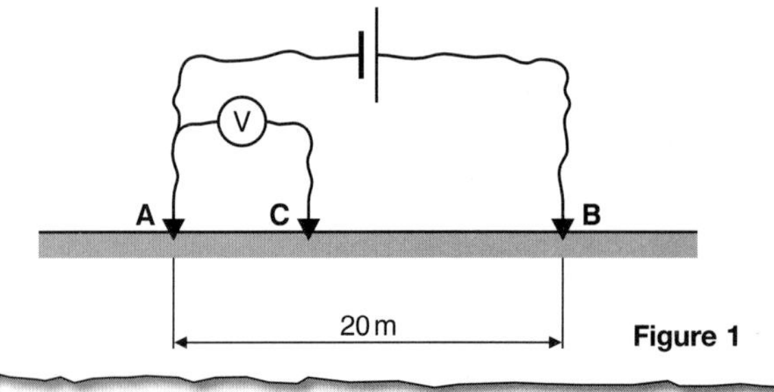

Figure 1

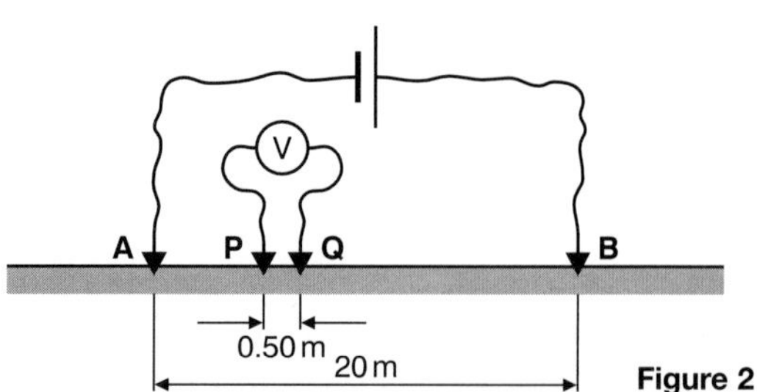

Figure 2

A test electrode **C** is then moved along the line joining the electrodes and the potential difference between **A** and **C** is measured. The geophysicist plots a graph of voltage against the distance. If the soil is of uniform resistivity the voltage increases linearly. Where there is an ore body, ions are released into the soil and this changes the gradient of the graph. The graph in **Figure 3** shows the results of one test using the method in **Figure 1**.

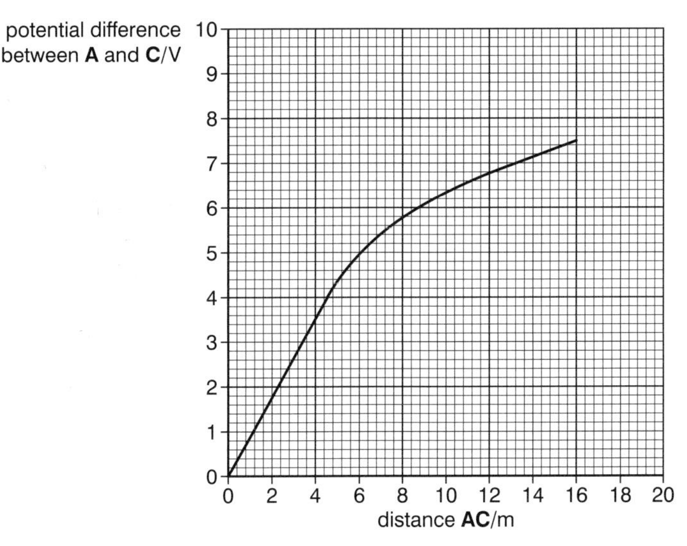

Figure 3

In the alternative approach, shown in **Figure 2**, two electrodes, **P** and **Q**, placed 0.50 m apart, are moved along the line between the electrodes **A** and **B**, and the variation of the voltage with position is used to locate the ore deposit.

Seismology

In seismology a small explosion is produced at the surface (**X** in **Figure 4**) and the electric pulse which causes the explosion is used to start a clock. The explosion sends a shock wave through the ground to a geophone some distance away (at **Y**).

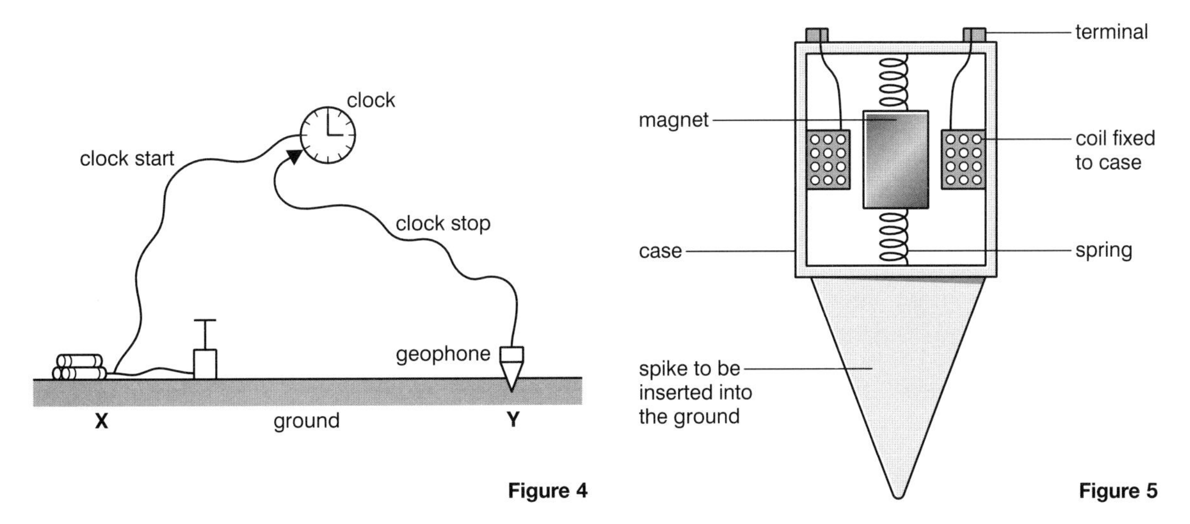

Figure 4

Figure 5

The structure of the geophone (simplified) is shown in **Figure 5**. The shock wave makes the coil in the geophone move up and down inducing a voltage which is used to stop the clock. The time taken for the wave to travel the distance **XY** is then known so that the speed of the shock wave between **X** and **Y** can be calculated. The speed of the shock wave changes from about 2000 m s^{-1} in soft soil to over 4000 m s^{-1} in ore deposits.

Examiner's hints for question 1

Part (a) You need to give a reason for this technique being:

- costly;
- hit and miss.

Part (b)(i) and (ii) Newton's law of gravitation should help you here.

Part (c) You should be thinking in terms of which source of radioactivity can penetrate layers of soil/rock/ores.

Q1

The following questions refer to the introductory paragraph.

(a) With reference to the task of searching for minerals by drilling holes, explain what the author means by '*a costly hit and miss exercise*'.

....

....

....

[2 marks]

(b) **(i)** State the quantity a geophysicist could measure to investigate variations in 'gravitational attraction'.

....

[1 mark]

(ii) Explain why the presence of an ore deposit could produce variations in gravitational attraction.

....

....

....

[2 marks]

(c) State and explain what type of radiation from radioactive ores is most likely to be measured using radiation detectors.

....

....

....

[2 marks]

[Total 7 marks]

Examiner's hints for question 2

Part (a) It may help to think whether the resistance between the electrode and the soil should be high or low.

Part (b) (i) Remember that in a voltage divider the p.d. is proportional to the resistance (for a constant current). You will need to consider the comparative resistances of metal ore with non-metallic rocks or soil.

(ii) The variation in the gradient of the graph should help you here.

(iii) Again use the graph and remember that **AB** = 20 m.

(iv) $V = IR$!

Part(c) You may draw tangents on the given graph to help you – you are sketching the variation of the potential gradient. You will be expected to mark in key values on this sketch.

Q2

The following questions refer to the paragraphs on '*Resistance or voltage measurements*'.

(a) State what is meant by the phrase '*good electrical contact*'.

....

[1 mark]

(b) The graph in **Figure 3** shows the result of one test using the method in **Figure 1**.

(i) State and explain whether you would recommend drilling nearer to **A** or nearer to **B**.

....

....

....

[2 marks]

(ii) Determine the approximate distance of the edge of the ore body from **A**.

....

[1 mark]

(iii) Determine the terminal potential difference of the supply used in the test that produced the data in **Figure 3**.

....

[1 mark]

(iv) The current through the battery was 5.0 mA. Calculate the resistance between the terminals **A** and **B**.

[2 marks]

(c) Sketch the graph that would be obtained for the region between **AB** when the circuit in **Figure 2** is used. Include a suitable scale on the axes.

[3 marks]

[Total 10 marks]

Examiner's hints for question 3

In this last part your written communication is assessed and so your ideas must be stated clearly. You need to watch your spelling, punctuation and grammar even more than usual.

Part (a) You are being asked to use your physics to answer this. You should think in terms of how the **shock wave** gets from the explosive to the geophone. Then you must consider why the magnet **(and springs)** will move differently from the case. You should try to remember the sort of motion that an object suspended from a spring will move with.

Part (b) Remind yourself about electromagnetic induction to help you here.

Part (c) Each element of this part of the question requires you to answer something:

- How does the energy travel from the explosive to the geophone? (type of wave and medium)
- Refer to the data in the passage to see in which material the wave travels fastest and give a good reason or reasons why this should be.

Q3

The following questions refer to the paragraphs on '*Seismology*'.

Explain:

(a) why movement of the Earth's surface makes the magnet in **Figure 5** move relative to the coil;

....

....

....

....

....

[3 marks]

(b) why relative movement between the magnet and the coil produces a voltage;

....

....

....

....

[2 marks]

(c) how energy is transmitted by a '*shock wave*' and suggest why the speed of the shock wave is different in soft soil and in ore deposits. You can gain up to 2 marks in this question for good written communication.

....

....

....

....

....

....

....

[6 marks]

[Total 11 marks]

The answers to these questions are on pages 91 and 92.

Exam question and student's answer

1 When a car has a brake test, the maximum braking force produced by operating the foot brake is measured together with the mass of the car.

In order to determine whether the brakes are satisfactory, the data are applied to a chart similar to that shown in Fig.1. This chart has three vertical lines, marked with axes.

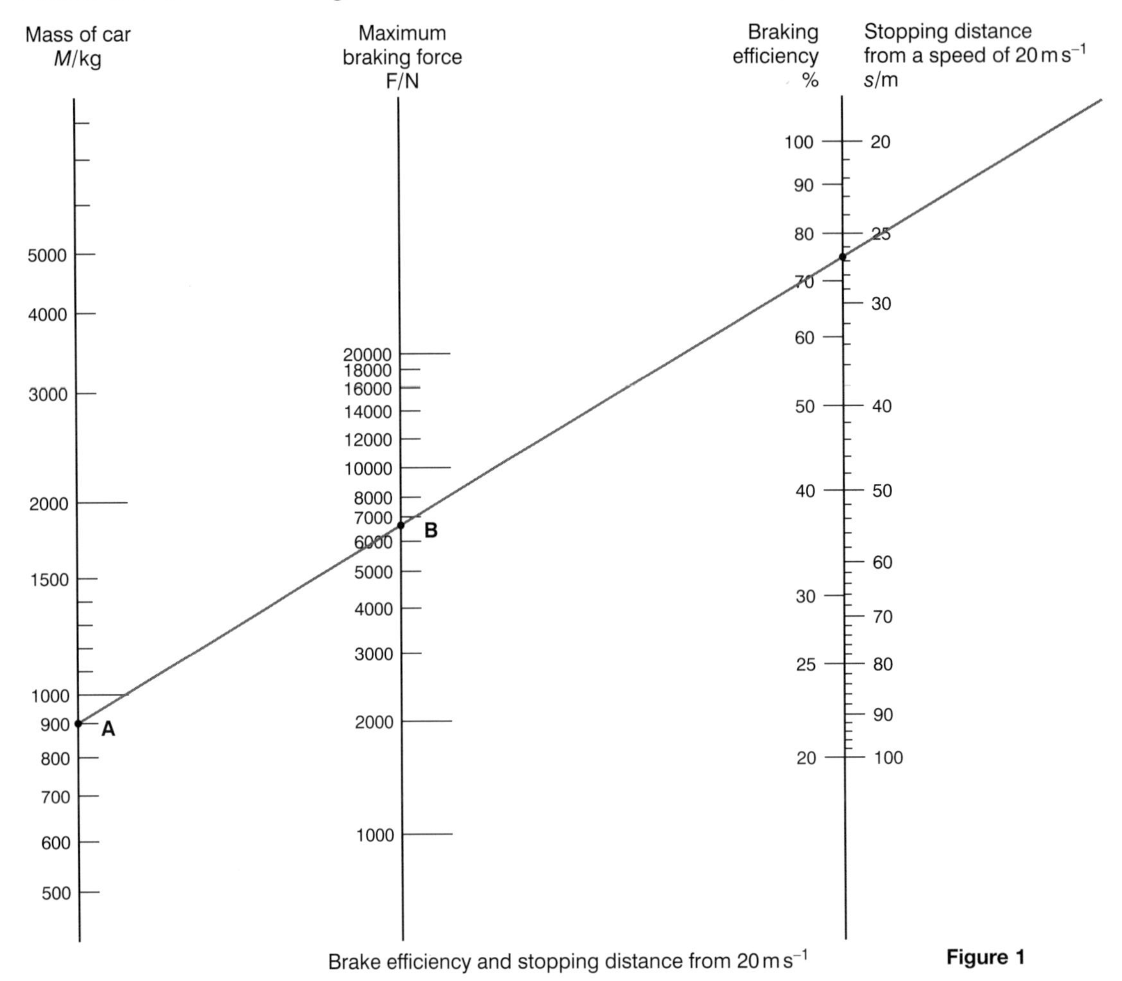

Brake efficiency and stopping distance from 20 m s^{-1} **Figure 1**

The left line is for the mass of the car and the central line is for the maximum braking force.

The right-hand line is for the braking efficiency and also for stopping distance from an initial speed of 20 m s^{-1}. The braking efficiency is defined by the equation

$$E = \frac{\text{deceleration of car}}{\text{acceleration of free fall}} \times 100\%$$

As an example of the use of the chart, a car of mass 900 kg is found to have a maximum braking force of 6700 N. The point **A** corresponding to the mass and the point **B** corresponding to the braking force are joined to give a straight, sloping line. The line is extended to cut the right-hand line so that the braking efficiency and the stopping distance may be read off.

(a) Determine

(i) the braking efficiency for a car of mass 900 kg having a maximum braking force of 6700 N.

✓ (1/1)

efficiency = 75%

(ii) the deceleration corresponding to this braking efficiency.

$75\% \times 9.8$ ✓ $\text{m s}^{-2} = 7.35$ ✓

deceleration = 7.35 m s^{-2} (2/2)

[3 marks]

(b) Show, by calculation, that the deceleration in **(a)(ii)** gives a stopping distance corresponding to the braking efficiency determined in **(a)(i)**.

$$\frac{20}{7.35} = 2.72$$

$$s = vt + \frac{1}{2}at^2$$

$$s = 20 \times 2.72 - \frac{1}{2} \times 7.35 \times 2.72^2$$

$= 27.2$ ✓ ✓ ✗ ∧

[3 marks]

(c) On a particular road surface, the stopping distance from 20 m s^{-1} is 50 m.

(i) Use the chart to determine the deceleration of the car.

$40\% \times 9.8 = 3.9$

deceleration = 3.9 ✓ m s^{-2}

(ii) Determine the effective braking force.

∧ force = 3700 ✗ N

[2 marks]

(d) The braking efficiency in **(a)** is for a dry road surface.

Suggest, with a reason, what happens to braking efficiency when the surface is wet.

The efficiency will be decreased ✓ because E ∝ deceleration

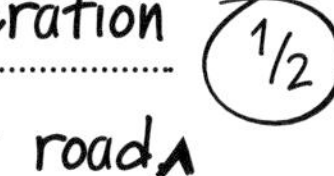

and deceleration will be less due to less grip on the wet road ∧

[2 marks]

[Total 10 marks]

How to score full marks

Part(a)(i)

The student **has drawn a very good construction line** passing through A and B and **has read the value accurately**. Marking the percentage value on her answer shows that she really knows what she is doing and gives the examiner the right signals too!

Part(a)(ii)

This is correct too but it would have been helpful if the student had shown where she had made her substitutions into the equation (E = deceleration of car/acceleration of free fall × 100%).

Part (b)

Although the answer is correct and she gets full marks for the calculation, **the student has not approached the question in the most direct way** because she calculated a value for t first. If she had used $v^2 = u^2 + 2as$ she could have answered this more efficiently.

She also loses the last mark because she does not comment that her stopping distance corresponds to the 75% determined in **part(a)(i)** – 75% appears to be approximately equivalent to 26.5 m (on the right hand data line of the figure) so her answer is close but not spot on.

Part (c)(i)

The student has correctly read the braking efficiency corresponding to a stopping distance of 50 m (40%). She has then correctly calculated the deceleration from the braking efficiency equation.

Part (c)(ii)

This answer lies outside the tolerance accepted by the examiners and, since **there is no evidence to suggest where it came from**, would not score any marks even if there were more than 1 mark available.

There are two ways of determining the braking force here:

- $F = ma$ gives
  $F = 900 \text{ kg} \times 3.9 \text{ m s}^{-2} = 3.5 \times 10^3 \text{ N}$
- Drawing a straight line from mass 900 kg to stopping distance 50 m gives 3600 N (approximately) – it looks as though the student used this latter method but didn't mark the figure!

Part(d)

This is quite a good answer and is, arguably, worth both marks. **The examiners were expecting examination candidates to say that the braking efficiency would be decreased because the stopping distance would be increased by a wet surface**. The student has failed to state that the braking distance increases but she has implied a reason for this – that the wet surface would mean a reduced (safe) deceleration.

Don't make these mistakes...

Don't forget to take a ruler, sharp 2H pencil, eraser, protractor and a calculator to the examination – you will not be allowed to share!

Your ruler should be 30 cm (and ideally transparent) with no dents on the edges.

Examination candidates often throw away marks with **lines that have obviously been drawn using too short a ruler** and trying to make two lines into one.

Do show your working by **marking in lines on diagrams** whenever construction may be needed. The student answered part (a)(i) really well by doing this and then failed to get the mark for (c)(ii) by not doing it!

Questions to try

You will need a sheet of graph paper to answer this question.

Examiner's hints for question 1

Part (a)

You will need to calculate the areas under the different sections of this graph to work out the distance travelled. The lines provided give you somewhere to show your working. You should divide the graph into 0.2 s regions, making a triangle and four trapeziums. This will allow you to calculate areas which are close approximations to the areas of the curve itself.

Remember:

the area of a triangle = ½ base × height

the area of a trapezium = sum of the lengths of the parallel sides × ½ the distance between them

Concentrate on making the maximum use of your graph paper and label your axes completely with both the numbers and the units. Plot your points accurately.

Part (b)

Take your answer from your calculated areas but do remember that they will be slight underestimates.

Part (c)

Mark your tangent on the curve at a time of 0.5 s and make sure that it is a **tangent – it only touches the curve at the required point**. Use a large gradient triangle to minimise your error in calculating the gradient.

Part (d)

Return to the original graph to take this reading.

Part (e)

With four marks for two reasons, the examiners are looking for a little more than statements of where the uncertainties occur here.

Part (f)

"Sketch" graphs will not require graph paper and therefore can be drawn in any convenient space on the page.

Think your way through the physics relating to an object falling through a viscous liquid. You should say **what causes the ball bearing to accelerate** in the first place and **why it reaches its terminal velocity** in a viscous liquid. You must then relate these ideas to the graphs you sketch.

Q1

This is a data analysis question and is about a ball bearing falling through viscous oil. The ball is released from rest at the top of a vertical column of oil, and its velocity is measured as it falls. The resulting velocity–time graph is shown.

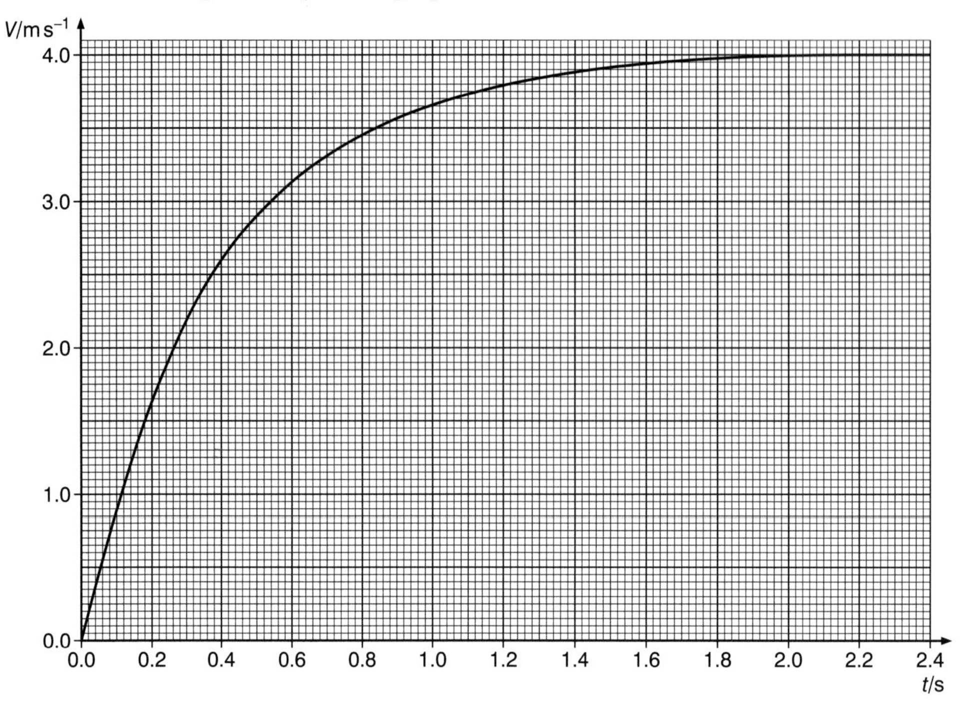

(a) Deduce from this graph, and draw, the corresponding displacement–time graph for the first second of descent, i.e. the graph showing how the position x of the ball, measured from the point of release, varies with the time t from release for $t = 0$ to 1 s. Six points are suggested.

....

....

....

....

....

....

....

[10 marks]

(b) How far has the ball fallen after 1 s?

....

....

[2 marks]

(c) Find the slope of your displacement–time graph at $t = 0.5$ s.

....

....

....

[6 marks]

(d) To what value of velocity in the given graph does your slope correspond? (Do not necessarily expect good numerical agreement here.)

....

....

[2 marks]

(e) Give two reasons for possible lack of agreement between your slope and the value from the given graph.

....

....

....

[4 marks]

(f) Two further experiments are performed with the same ball bearing but with two different oils; an oil *X* which is thicker (more viscous) than the original oil, and an oil *Y* which is thinner than the original.

(i) Sketch on common axes the velocity–time curves you would expect for oils *X* and *Y*. Clearly label each curve.

(ii) Show on the same axes the curve for the original oil for comparison.

(iii) Explain any differences between the curves and any features they have in common.

[You can assume that the resistance to motion experienced by the ball is proportional to its velocity in each case.]

....

....

....

....

....

....

[6 marks]

[Total 30 marks]

The answers to these questions are on pages 92 and 93.

Exam question and student's answer

1 The diagram shows a water skier being pulled at a steady speed in a straight line. Her mass plus the mass of the ski is 65 kg. The pull of the tow-rope on her is 520 N.

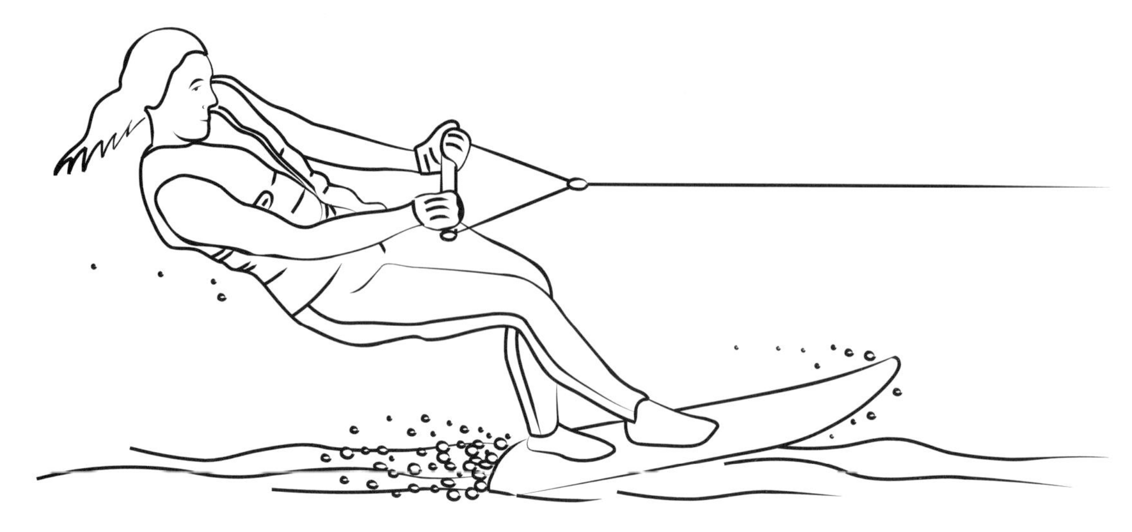

(a) (i) What are the horizontal and vertical components *X* and *Y* of the push of the water on the ski? (Ignore air resistance.)

vertical $65 \times 9.8 = 637$ N

horizontal = 520 N ✓ 1/1

(ii) Her weight and the 520 N towing force exert moments around the point on the ski through which the resultant of *X* and *Y* act.

Explain how she can remain in equilibrium as she is towed along if the size of the towing force varies.

When the horizontal towing force increases, the skier should stand further back to increase the anticlockwise moment of her weight to balance the clockwise moment from the towing force and vice versa. ✓ ^ ^

[4 marks]

(b) Later, while still being towed, she moves in a curved path from behind the boat to approach a ramp from which she makes a jump, remaining in the air for over two seconds. Describe the force which enables her to accelerate centripetally as she moves in a curved path.

Why does she feel "weightless" while in the air during her jump?

The towing force can be parallel to the water surface and making an angle to the forward direction at the same time. Its vertical component provides the centripetal force. ✗✗ During the jump, she exerts a force on the ramp and the ramp exerts on her an equal and opposite force. Until this force gets smaller than her weight due to gravity, she feels weightless. ∧

[3 marks]

(c) After her jump she again moves with her original velocity, experiencing a towing force of 520 N. Suddenly, she lets go of the tow-rope. Calculate her initial deceleration. Why does her deceleration reduce as she slows down?

When F = 520 N, system in equilibrium.

When let go of rope y-component = −520 N

−520 = ma ✓

a = −8 m s^{-2} ✓

As skier slows down, the viscous force from the water decreases, so deceleration decreases. ✓

[3 marks]

(d) An observer notices that the waves she produces approaching the shore diffract as they pass through a gap leading to a boatyard. The diffraction of electro-magnetic waves is involved when we collect information about stars and galaxies. Explain how light diffracted through gratings can yield information about distant stars and galaxies. You may be awarded a mark for the clarity of your answer.

The interference pattern is shown by diffraction of light through a grating. The fringe separation can be used to calculate the wavelength of light using: $d\sin\theta = n\lambda$ ✓

By using $\Delta\lambda/\lambda = v/c$ the recession velocity of the star can be calculated. ✓ Where there is a red shift, longer wavelength (positive $\Delta\lambda$), the star is moving away from the Earth and vice versa. ✓

[5 marks]

[Total 15 marks]

How to score full marks

Part (a)(i)

 This answer is fine but the student should have referred to X and Y.

Part (a)(ii)

 This is correct but too vague an answer. You should start by explaining that the tension in the rope applies a clockwise moment and this is balanced by the skier's weight providing an anticlockwise moment. If the tension increases, equilibrium can only be restored by increasing the perpendicular distance from the weight to the pivot or decreasing the distance from the tension to the pivot. If the tension decreases, the weight must be brought closer to the pivot or the tension moved further away.

Part (b)

 No, it is the force of the water on the base of the water ski (and directed to the centre of the circular arc) that provides the centripetal force.

The second part of the answer is nearly right – you should say "...when she is in the air the only significant force acting on the skier is her weight – since she has no reaction acting on her she feels "weightless".

Part (c)

 A good answer and nearly excellent. The student has only given his final answer to one significant figure when the data was given to two significant figures – in this case the student had already been penalised in an earlier question and so a **significant figure penalty** was not applied.

Part (d)

 Although this looks like a good answer it really isn't focused enough. You should concentrate on what the light tells us about distant stars. The first mark is for stating that the wavelength of the light is measured – and this does give information about the distant stars.

 Mention of the Doppler effect would focus this answer a little more and gain a mark. You should also say that the **spectral lines tell us what chemical elements are present in stars** – when they are shifted we can work out how fast the star is travelling relative to the Earth and whether it is moving towards or away from the Earth.

 Because the communication is good and the physics used is accurate, the candidate scores the mark for quality of written communication here.

Don't make these mistakes...

Don't convince yourself that your answer is correct simply because you know that you are writing good physics. **Your answer must be relevant too**. You should focus on what is the key aspect of a question – in part (d), the information about distant stars and galaxies that the light conveys.

Do try to be open-minded about the range of topics in synoptic questions. Who would have thought the examiners could have linked forces on a water skier to the Doppler effect and light! **These examinations really do test your breadth of knowledge and the links between topics** – sometimes the links can be a little artificial and so you must **keep alert** and not make up your own questions!

Questions to try

Examiner's hints for question 1
Part (a)(i)
A simple statement of nuclear binding energy is needed here – there is no need to try to explain what is meant by the definition.
Part (a)(ii)
This is where the explanation comes in and you do need to explain why an increase in binding energy per nucleon means energy released.
Part (a)(iii)
Don't forget to calculate the **total** difference in binding energy here.
Part (b)(i)
You will need to convert the energy from MeV into joules in order to apply the Planck relationship.
Part (b)(ii)
The Doppler relationship needs to be used – easiest to work in terms of frequency rather than wavelength here.

Q1

The graph shows the variation of nuclear binding energy per nucleon with nucleon number.

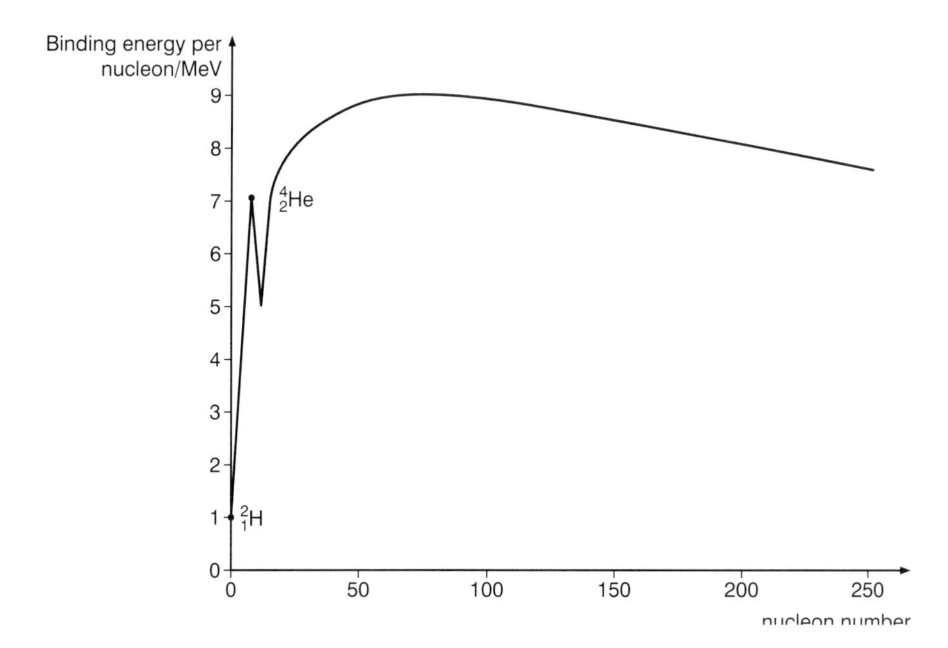

a) **(i)** State what is meant by the phrase *nuclear binding energy*.

....

....

....

[2 marks]

(ii) Use the graph to explain, in terms of binding energy, why the formation of $^{4}_{2}He$ (helium) by the fusion of two $^{2}_{1}H$ (heavy hydrogen) nuclei results in the production of energy.

....

....

....

[2 marks]

(iii) Use data from the graph to estimate the amount of energy, in MeV, released when two $^{2}_{1}H$ nuclei fuse.

[3 marks]

(b) The reaction in part **(a)(iii)** takes place in a star that is moving away from the Earth at a speed of 8.0×10^{6} m s^{-1}.

(i) Assuming that all the energy is released as a single gamma ray, determine its wavelength.

charge on an electron $e = -1.6 \times 10^{-19}$ C

Planck constant $h = 6.6 \times 10^{-34}$ J s

speed of electromagnetic radiation $c = 3.0 \times 10^{8}$ m s^{-1}

[3 marks]

(ii) Calculate the difference between the frequency of the gamma ray that would be measured by an observer on Earth and the actual frequency. State whether this would be an increase or a decrease.

[3 marks]

[Total 13 marks]

Examiner's hints for question 2

Part (a)(i)

This is a uniform field so don't try using a radial equation (one with π in it).

Part (a)(ii)

Try relating the field strength to the force per unit charge.

Part (a)(iii)

You can either work using the conservation of energy or you can calculate the acceleration and use the equations of motion.

Part (b)(i)

Remember that Fleming's left hand rule applies to conventional current – positive charge.

Part (b)(ii)

The usual circular motion explanation is needed here – concentrate on the directional side of the motion.

Part (b)(iii)

You are going to have to juggle around with the equation for force on a charge in a magnetic field and the centripetal force equation.

Part (c)

This is referring to the motion in the magnetic field of **part (b)** – you will need to argue this in terms of your equation in **(b)(iii)**.

Q2

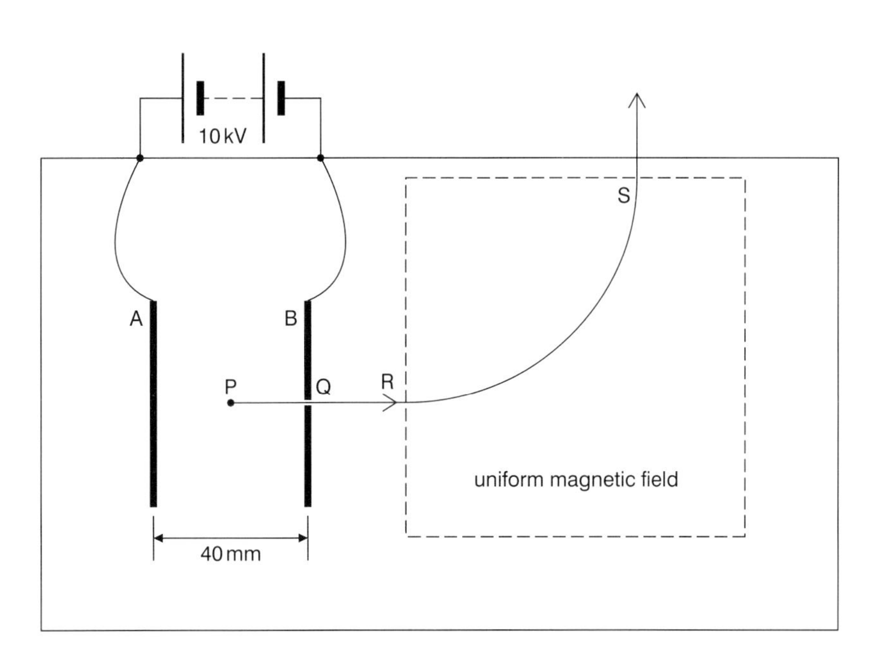

A positive ion with a mass of 3.4×10^{-26} kg and a charge of 3.2×10^{-19} C is initially at rest at a point P, midway between two parallel conducting plates, A and B which are separated by 40 mm. The ion is accelerated and passes through a hole Q in plate B. It enters a magnetic field of uniform flux density 0.10 T at R. After following a circular path the ion leaves the field at S. Assume that the magnetic field is uniform everywhere within the dotted rectangle and that the space within the solid rectangle is evacuated.

(a) (i) Calculate the electric field strength between the plates AB.

....

....

(ii) Calculate the force on the ion due to the electric field.

....

....

(iii) Show that the speed of the ion just after it has passed through the hole at Q is 3.1×10^5 m s^{-1}.

....

....

....

[5 marks]

(b) (i) State the direction of the magnetic field.

....

(ii) Explain why the ion follows a circular path in the magnetic field.

....

....

(iii) Show that the radius of the circular path is proportional to the momentum of the ion and calculate the value of the radius.

....

....

....

....

[6 marks]

(c) Explain how, if at all, the trajectory would be different for an ion with a slightly greater mass but carrying the same charge.

....

....

....

....

[2 marks]

[Total 13 marks]

The answers to these questions are on pages 93 and 94.

12 Graphs and Maths

Graph plotting

This is one of the most basic tools used in A level physics and you can often improve your skills here by following a few simple ideas:

- **Aim to fill the graph paper as fully as you can** – you will notice any errors in your readings more easily on a larger scale, and it also reduces 'uncertainties' caused by inaccurate drawing.

- **Do not use scales which are multiples of odd numbers like 3 or 7,** as it becomes almost impossible to plot decimal values with such scales – for example, on a 0,3,6,9 scale 0.1 will be 1/3 of a small square. You should use multiples of 5 or 10 if possible (4 is usually viewed as being acceptable but it's not one of my favourite scales for checking answers!).

- **Do not include the origin on your graph unless you really need to** (it is likely to mean that you have all your points bunched up in the top corner of the page and cancels out the idea of using the whole graph page).

- **Label your axes with both the numbers and the units** but don't forget that if you apply some function to the quantity then you must also apply it to the unit too. (For example, if you are plotting the square of the period then if the period is in s the square of the period will be in s^2.

- **When you take the logs of quantities remember that the log has no unit.**

Straight-line graphs are examiners' favourites because they don't have to worry about the smoothness of a curved line – which is always difficult to assess.

Try to convert any relationship into $y = mx + c$ (where m is the gradient and c the intercept on the y-axis). Often equations don't look like this but with a little bit of algebraic manipulation they can almost always be put in this form.

For example, the electrical power equation $P = I^2R$ could be plotted as a straight line graph of P (y-axis) against I^2 (x-axis) if R was constant (e.g. a conductor at constant temperature).

The emf equation $E = I(R + r)$ multiplies out to give $E = IR + Ir$ [$= V + Ir$].

A graph of V (y-axis) against I (x-axis) will be of gradient $-r$ and intercept on the y–axis of E.

Compare $y = mx + c$

with $V = -rI + E$

The equation for the period of a loaded spring is $T = 2\pi\sqrt{\frac{m}{k}}$.

If you square this you get: $T^2 = 4\pi^2\frac{m}{k}$

So a graph of T^2 against m will be a straight line of gradient $\frac{4\pi^2}{k}$. It will pass through the origin, showing that $T^2 \propto m$.

Logs

Logs are the graph plotter's friend! They provide us with a way of making powers palatable.

The equation $T = 2\pi\sqrt{\frac{m}{k}}$ can also be written as $T = 2\pi\left(\frac{m}{k}\right)^{\frac{1}{2}}$

This may not look very good but if we take logs of this we get:

$\log(T) = \log(2\pi) + \frac{1}{2}\log(m) - \frac{1}{2}\log(k)$

or $\log T = \frac{1}{2}\log m + \text{constant}$

This means that if you plot log T against log m you get a linear graph of gradient $\frac{1}{2}$ and with intercept of value = $\log(2\pi) - \frac{1}{2}\log k$. You can work out the value of k from this.

The very best thing about using logs is that **it helps you to find the powers in relationships**.

For example, it may be suggested that the power output of a lamp is related to the absolute temperature by the equation:

$P = T^n$

If you take logs of this you get $\log(P) = n\log(T)$

The gradient of a graph of $\log(P)$ against $\log(T)$ will be of value n – so you can find n fairly easily experimentally.

Exponentials

As you have seen in chapters 5 and 7, exponentials are quite important in physics. **It is fairly easy to deal with exponentials by taking logs to base e (or "ln" on calculators)**.

For example the equation for the discharge of a capacitor is:

$Q = Q_0 e^{-\frac{t}{RC}}$

By taking logs to base e you get

$\ln Q = \ln Q_0 - \frac{t}{RC}$

so a graph of ln Q (y-axis) against t (x-axis) will give a straight line of negative gradient $= \frac{1}{RC}$ and intercept on the ln Q axis of ln Q_0.

Taking the antilog of the intercept value (e^x button on your calculator) gives you a value for Q_0.

Errors and uncertainties

Although **these two names actually mean the same thing,** the word uncertainty is the better term since it cannot be confused with the word "mistake".

When you measure any quantity you cannot actually measure its true value. Human senses have limitations and the instruments that you use are not perfect (nor can they ever be). So it is useful to calculate what the uncertainty in your value is. **This is a measure of how close you judge your answer is to the true value.**

There are two types of uncertainty that we might consider. These are called **systematic** and **random** uncertainties.

Systematic uncertainties are those that are due to the system of measurement that we use. For example, if a meter has been miscalibrated it will never give you the true value even if you could read it perfectly. **Systematic uncertainties shift all your readings in the same direction** but you cannot easily detect them without using a second set of apparatus – then of course, you don't know which is right or wrong! The systematic uncertainty determines the **accuracy** of your readings (how far they are from the true value) and is not helped by repeated reading using the same apparatus.

Random uncertainties have many causes but are distributed around a mean value and usually result from your inability to take the same measurement in exactly the same way each time. Examples of sources of random uncertainties are using an instrument with a scale of low precision or having a slow reaction time. **Random uncertainties can be reduced by taking a series of readings and finding the average (mean) value.** These uncertainties affect the **precision** of your answer (the number of significant figures that you are justified in quoting).

When you perform an "error" analysis, **you are assessing the random uncertainties** not the systematic ones.

How far out is your reading?

It is important that your uncertainty limits are large enough to include the true value of the quantity that you are measuring. For analogue meters, rulers, thermometers, etc., it is best to quote the uncertainty as being the smallest scale division (graduation). You are likely to estimate the reading to better than this but what you are saying is that your answer is definitely within this uncertainty range.

For example, when you read a single value on a ruler to be 28 mm you should quote the value as being

(28±1) mm

This says that the reading is definitely between 27 mm and 29 mm.

- **Always quote your uncertainty to the same number of decimal places as the quantity that you are measuring.**

When you are using a **digital meter** do not be fooled into believing that the uncertainty is the least significant digit. The uncertainty will depend on the tolerance of the electronic components in the meter. A good rule of thumb is to say that the uncertainty is at the level of the next to least significant digit.

Suppose a digital ammeter shows value of 2.46 A. You should quote this as (2.5±0.1) A.

Your reading may well be better than this but you are indicating to the examiner that **you recognise that there are reasonable uncertainties even when using digital meters.**

In a similar way, when you use a **digital stopwatch** to time 20 oscillations as taking 14.23 seconds – don't fool yourself that this precision is valid! Your **reaction time is likely to be of the order of 0.1 s** and so you should use this as your uncertainty and quote the time as being (14.2±0.1) s.

The value 0.1 s is called the **absolute uncertainty** in the time;

$\frac{0.1}{14.2} \times 100\% = 0.7\%$ is called the **percentage uncertainty** in the time.

Note that **absolute uncertainties have units while percentage uncertainties do not.**

Improving the level of uncertainty

By taking a series of readings you are increasing the probability that your average value is closer to the true value (assuming no systematic errors are present). This will reduce your level of uncertainty and increase your confidence that you are measuring well.

Some examination boards like you to quote a **simple standard uncertainty** as being

$$\frac{\text{maximum reading} - \text{minimum reading}}{\text{number of readings taken}}$$

(this is an approximation to a more elaborate statistical formula but it's OK for A level physics!).

Suppose you measure a mass as being 0.140 kg, 0.142 kg and 0.143 kg. The simple standard uncertainty for these values is (0.143 kg – 0.140 kg)/3 = 0.001 kg so you should quote the mass as being (0.142±0.001) kg.

Combinations of uncertainties

Although there are formulae for calculating uncertainties it is quite easy to calculate them just by using **your measured values** and **your estimates of the absolute uncertainty in each value.**

To measure the resistivity of a material, the current in and voltage across a wire are measured to be (6.6 ± 0.1) A and (2.6 ± 0.1) V. The length of the wire (l) is (0.800 ± 0.002) m and its diameter (d) is (0.50 ± 0.01) mm. Using these values the resistivity, ρ, can be calculated, together with a value for the uncertainty in the measurement.

$$\rho = \frac{RA}{l}$$

$$= \frac{V\pi d^2}{4Il}$$

Substituting the values into this we get a value for ρ:

$$\rho = \frac{2.6\text{V} \times \pi \times (0.50 \times 10^{-3}\text{ m})^2}{4 \times 6.6\text{ A} \times 0.80\text{ m}}$$

$$= 9.6 \times 10^{-8}\ \Omega\text{ m}$$

A second, larger, value that would be just possible to obtain for ρ can be found by making each of the quantities on the top of the equation larger by its maximum uncertainty and by making each of the quantities on the bottom of the equation smaller by its uncertainty:

$$\rho_{big} = \frac{2.7\text{ V} \times \pi \times (0.51 \times 10^{-3}\text{ m})^2}{4 \times 6.5\text{ A} \times 0.798\text{ m}}$$

$$= 10.6 \times 10^{-8}\ \Omega\text{ m}$$

A third, smaller, value that would be just possible to obtain for ρ can be found by making each of the quantities on the top of the equation smaller by its maximum uncertainty and by making each of the quantities on the bottom of the equation larger by its uncertainty:

$$\rho_{small} = \frac{2.5\text{ V} \times \pi \times (0.49 \times 10^{-3}\text{ m})^2}{4 \times 6.7\text{ A} \times 0.802\text{ m}}$$

$$= 8.7 \times 10^{-8}\ \Omega\text{ m}$$

The average difference between the ρ value calculated assuming no uncertainties and that calculated assuming maximum uncertainties (in the same overall direction) is approximately $1.0 \times 10^{-8}\ \Omega$ m and so the value that you should quote is

$$\rho = (9.6 \pm 1.0) \times 10^{-8}\ \Omega\text{ m}.$$

Questions to try

Examiner's hint for question 1

- You need to manipulate the equation to leave A on its own. Although doing this complicates E, it will then give you a straight-line graph.

The emf of a thermocouple is given by the equation $E = AT + BT^2$. By measuring E at various values of T we should be able to plot a graph that will give us the values of A and B.

Here are some typical values:

E / V	0.92	2.64	5.44	9.21	14.0	19.7	27.4	35.0
T / °C	10	20	30	40	50	60	70	80

(a) Add an extra row to the table to give values that will allow you to draw a straight-line graph.

[3 marks]

(b) Plot this graph and use it to calculate values for A and B.

[12 marks]

Examiner's hint for question 2

- It's probably easiest to take log to base e of the ratio of the voltages in order to get rid of the exponential part of the equation.

The rate of discharge of a capacitor through a resistor can be used to measure the capacitor's capacitance C using the equation

$$V = V_0 e^{-\frac{t}{RC}}$$

At time 0 s the voltage across the capacitor (V_0) is measured to be (5.8 ± 0.2) V. After (50 ± 1) s it is measured to be (1.2 ± 0.2) V. The resistor has a value of (1000 ± 50) Ω.

Calculate a value for the capacitor and the uncertainty in your value.

[7 marks]

Examiner's hints for question 3

- This question is really quite synoptic in that it ties together several aspects of physics that you might meet in different areas – not least, it uses the skills of graph plotting and error analysis.
- The question is quite structured and each part helps with subsequent ones!
- You will see from the units that you need to do a little work on the temperatures to be able to work in kelvin and on the volumes to work in m^3.
- In **part (a)(i)** you are helped with *R* in part **(c)**, and this is probably the most difficult unit. So this part is an easy opener for two marks.
- Before you can tackle **part (a)(ii)** you must think about the best way to get a straight line graph and to **make use of the gradient to calculate the unknowns**.
- In **part (b)**, it is best to consider the possible uncertainty in your gradient in order to work out the uncertainty in *nR*. To do this you must draw in a **line that would be just possible** as well the best straight line. **The uncertainty in the gradient will then be the difference between the gradients of the two lines**.
- For **part (c)** you know the value of *nR* , so you can now easily calculate *n*. You can work out the percentage error in the gradient, **so the percentage error in *n* will simply be the percentage error in the gradient + the percentage error in *R***.

The diagram shows the arrangement by which a gas is heated inside a large, sealed glass syringe.

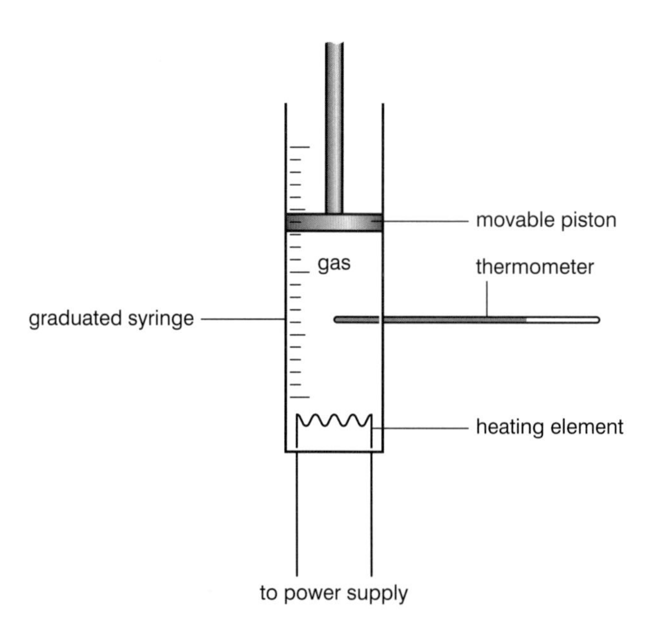

The temperature of the gas is measured in °C with a liquid-in-glass thermometer and the volume of the gas is read directly from the position of the movable piston on the graduations on the syringe.

The pressure on the gas is atmospheric of value $(1.1 \pm 0.1) \times 10^5$ Pa.

A student used this apparatus and obtained the following results:

temperature / °C	volume / cm^3
0	40.4
20	42.3
40	46.0
60	49.2
80	52.2
100	55.4

(a) The ideal gas equation may be written as $pV = nRT$.

(i) State the meaning of each of the quantities in this equation and give consistent units for each of the terms. [2 marks]

(ii) Use the data the student obtained to find a value for the product nR. [12 marks]

(b) Estimate the absolute uncertainty in your value for nR. [4 marks]

(c) The accepted value for $R = (8.3 \pm 0.1)$ J mol^{-1} K^{-1}. Calculate a value for n together with the absolute uncertainty in this quantity. [7 marks]

The answers to these questions are on pages 94 and 95.

13 Answers to Questions to try

Notes: A tick against a part of an answer indicates where a mark would be awarded.

Chapter 1 Circular Motion

Q1 How to score full marks

(a) Although the speed is constant, the direction of the astronaut is continually changing and so there is a change in his velocity (vector). ✓ A change in velocity means there is some form of acceleration ✓ – which requires a force to bring it about. ✓

(b) $F = \frac{mv^2}{r}$ where F is the horizontal force on the astronaut, m is his mass, v his speed and r the radius of the circle in which he is moving. ✓

(c) $a = \frac{v^2}{r}$ ✓ $\therefore 4 \times 9.8\ \text{m s}^{-2} = \frac{v^2}{20\ \text{m}}$

$\therefore v^2 = 4 \times 9.8\ \text{m s}^{-2} \times 20\ \text{m}$

$\therefore v = \sqrt{4 \times 9.8\ \text{m s}^{-2} \times 20\ \text{m}} = 28\ \text{m s}^{-1}$ ✓

> **Examiner's comment**
> I have included all units in this calculation for completeness – you would not be penalised for missing out the units in the middle of calculations but **the final unit must always be included.**

Q2 How to score full marks

(a)

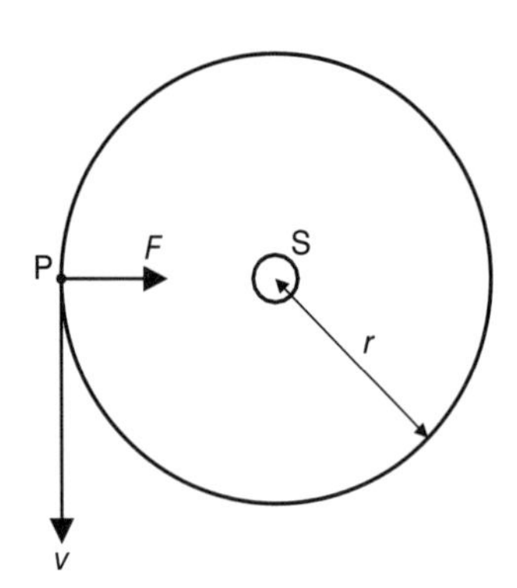

(b) **(i)** $a = \frac{v^2}{r}$ ✓

(ii) $F = ma = \frac{mv^2}{r}$ ✓✓

(iii) $F = G\frac{mM}{r^2}$ ✓

(c) **(i)** $T = \frac{2\pi r}{v}$ ✓

(ii) $G\frac{Mm}{r^2} = \frac{mv^2}{r}$

$G\frac{M}{r} = v^2$

Speed = $\frac{\text{circumference}}{\text{time}}$, so:

$\frac{4\pi^2 r^2}{T^2} = G\frac{M}{r}$ ✓✓

$\frac{4\pi^2 r^3}{GM} = T^2$

> **Examiner's comment**
> Although there are no words included in this answer the style of the question has meant that explanations are simply done mathematically.

Chapter 2 Oscillations

Q1 How to score full marks

> **Examiner's comment**
> The first part is probably tackled most easily by finding the period (60 s/6000) and then calculating f as $\frac{1}{T}$.

$f = \frac{6000}{60} = 100\ \text{Hz}$ ✓

(complete numerical answer with unit)

LT is the distance from one extreme to the other (peak to peak) and this is twice the amplitude. Amplitude = 4.3 cm. ✓

Maximum acceleration (a_0) is given by:

$a_0 = -(2\pi f)^2 A$

$a_0 = -(2\pi \times 100\ \text{Hz})^2 \times 4.3 \times 10^{-2}\ \text{m}$ ✓

$a_0 = -1.7 \times 10^4\ \text{m s}^{-1}$ ✓

Since the acceleration and displacement are proportional (definition of s.h.m.) they will be zero at the same place (zero displacement) so this will be midway between T and L. ✓

Q2 How to score full marks

a) (i)

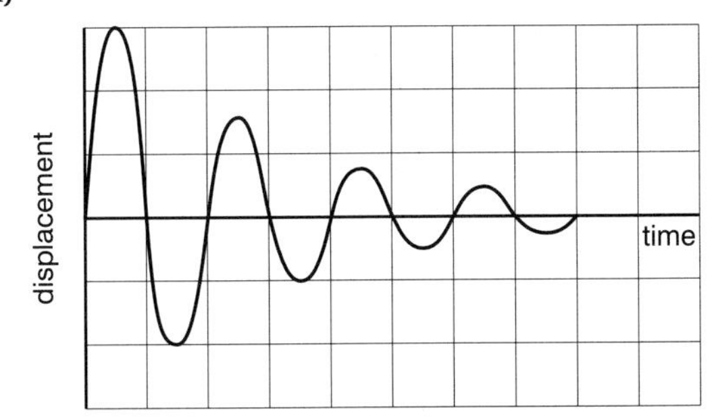

> **Examiner's comments**
> Constant time period shown ✓
> Decay in amplitude shown ✓

(ii) The velocity is given by the gradient, ✓ which changes with time.

b) In car suspension systems ✓ immersing them in oil damps the springs.✓ This prevents the car from giving a bouncy journey as it passes over a rough road surface. ✓

> **Examiner's comment**
> Many other systems may be suggested in part (b) but they must benefit from damping. There would probably be a mark each for (i) naming a system benefiting from damping, (ii) explaining how damping is achieved and (iii) explaining the benefit of damping – the question has structured your answer for you.

Q3 How to score full marks

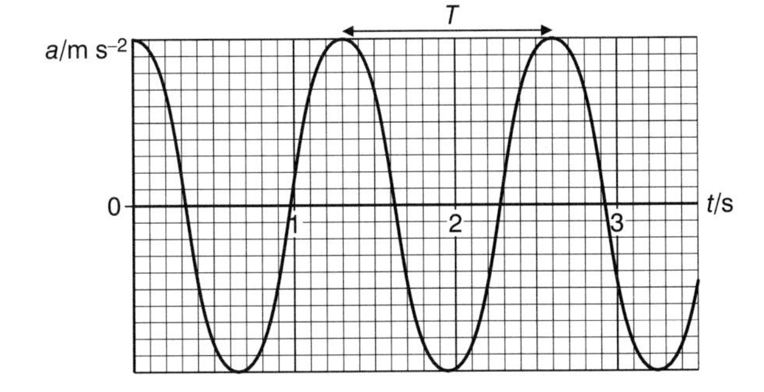

The frequency = $\frac{1}{\text{period}}$ – this is marked T on the graph: $f = \frac{1}{1.3}$ s = 0.77 Hz ✓ (there would probably be a tolerance of ± 0.03 Hz given here)

The **gradient** of the velocity–time curve gives the acceleration (as always) and so the gradient must be a positive maximum at time 0 s and a maximum when changing from positive to negative at 0.3 s etc. It should look like:

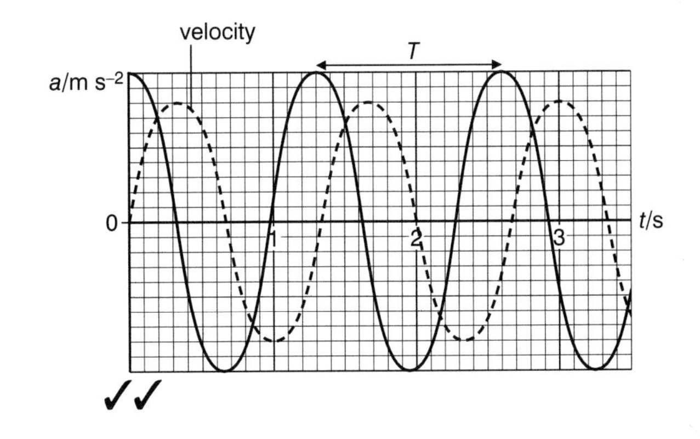

✓✓

> **Examiner's comments**
> It would be unlikely for the velocity and the acceleration scales to be the same so I have drawn them different sizes. You would not be penalised for making them look the same. There are two marks for this part. The graph as shown would gain both marks but an inverted velocity graph would gain a compensation mark.

Since $F = ma$ the shape of the force–time graph will be identical to the acceleration–time graph (although, again, it would not need to have the same amplitude). ✓✓

You need to use the equation for the period of a mass on a spring:

$$T = 2\pi\sqrt{\frac{m}{k}}$$

With $m \rightarrow 2m$ and $k \rightarrow 4k$ you get

$$T' = 2\pi\sqrt{\frac{2m}{4k}} = \sqrt{\frac{2}{4}} \times T$$ ✓

$$T' = 0.71 \times 1.2 \text{ s}$$

$$T' = 0.85 \text{ s}$$ ✓

Chapter 3 Gravitational Fields

Q1 How to score full marks

(a) **(i)** The acceleration is increasing with time. ✓

(ii) The gradient of the graph increases with time. ✓

(iii) **Either** the gravitational field strength of the Earth decreases with distance from the Earth ✓ **or** the mass of the rocket becomes less as the fuel is used up.✓

> **Examiner's comment**
> Each of these reasons is true and the increased acceleration is the result of the combined effect of the two factors.

(b) **(i)** From Newton's law of gravitation:

$F = G\dfrac{Mm}{r^2}$ ✓

$\therefore F = \dfrac{6.7 \times 10^{-11}\,\text{N m}^2\,\text{kg}^{-2} \times 3.9 \times 10^3\,\text{kg} \times 6.0 \times 10^{24}\,\text{kg}}{(1.0 \times 10^7\,\text{m})^2}$ ✓

($= 1.6 \times 10^4$ N as required)

(ii) Choose a point on the curve such as (1.0×10^7m, 1.6×10^4 N) and find the product $FR^2 = 1.6 \times 10^{18}$ N m^2 ✓

Choose a second point such as (4.0×10^7 m, 0.1×10^4 N) and find the new product $FR^2 = 1.6 \times 10^{18}$ N m^2 ✓

Since these two values are equal the data are consistent, ✓ FR^2 = constant.✓

Examiner's comment

If you found that your values were not equal (or, at least, very close) you should admit that this is the case. If the reason for this is a misreading then you would still score some marks for doing the right things. Ignoring errors and pretending what you have done is correct will always be heavily penalised.

(iii) You should attempt to measure the area under the curve. Each "large" square has an area of 1.0×10^{10} J ✓ ($= 0.2 \times 10^4$ N $\times 0.5 \times 10^7$ m). There are approximately 12 squares ✓ (by counting and estimating) therefore the **increase** in potential energy will be 12×10^{10} J. ✓

Examiner's comments

There would be a tolerance of perhaps ± 1 square in the accepted answer – since you cannot be expected to calculate the answer accurately from the graph. It is possible to calculate the change in potential energy from:

$$V_g = -GMm\left(\frac{1}{R_1} - \frac{1}{R_2}\right)$$

$$= 1.21 \times 10^{11}\ \text{J}$$

Note that since g.p.e. is defined to be zero at infinity (relative to the mass setting up the gravitational field) this means that the system has done work in attracting the mass from infinity and so the potential energy is reduced (below zero and so negative). The further from the Earth that the rocket is the less negative potential energy the rocket has – this is an increase in potential energy.

(iv) $F = \dfrac{mv^2}{R}$ ✓

$v = \sqrt{\dfrac{FR}{m}} = \sqrt{\dfrac{4.5 \times 10^3\,\text{N} \times 4.0 \times 10^7\,\text{m}}{3.9 \times 10^3\,\text{kg}}}$

$= 6.8 \times 10^3$ m s^{-1}

(v) At a higher orbit the gravitational force providing the centripetal force is reduced. ✓ Consequently the velocity and kinetic energy will fall too.✓ Thus the chemical energy does not supply the increase in potential energy alone – some comes from the decrease in kinetic energy.✓

Chapter 4 Electric Fields

Q1 How to score full marks

The electric field strength is the potential gradient and so the gradient of the tangent to this graph must be found at 1.5×10^{-10} m ✓

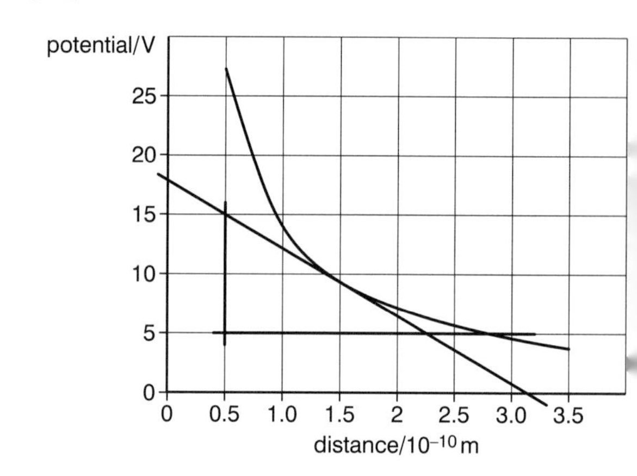

$$\text{field strength} = \frac{(15 - 5)\ \text{V}}{(0.5 - 2.2) \times 10^{-10}\ \text{m}} = -5.9 \times 10^{10}\ \text{V m}^{-1}$$

Examiner's comment

There would be some tolerance over the final answer here (probably at least 0.5×10^{10} V m^{-1}) since the grid is quite coarse. You should attempt to draw as large a gradient triangle as possible to improve the precision of your answer.

Q2 How to score full marks

(a) The arrangement of the lines of force indicates the direction, strength and uniformity of field (any two of these ✓✓)

(b) parallel lines (cloud to Earth) ✓
equally spaced ✓
directed downwards ✓

(c) $E = \frac{V}{d} \therefore V = Ed = 5.0 \times 10^4 \text{ N C}^{-1} \times 0.75 \times 10^3 \text{ m}$
$= 3.8 \times 10^7 \text{ V}$ ✓

Examiner's comment
The final answer in (c) is given to two significant figures to indicate that it is no more precise than the data from which it was derived (3.7×10^7 V is equally acceptable). The unit of electric field strength (N C^{-1}) is equivalent to V m^{-1}, meaning that the m and m^{-1} cancel to leave V as the correct unit for potential difference.

Chapter 5 Capacitors

Q1 How to score full marks

(a) **(i)** $V \propto Q$ (since $C = Q/V$) so you should draw a straight line of positive gradient ✓ passing through the origin. ✓

(ii) Capacitance is the ratio of the charge to the potential ✓ which is given by the reciprocal of the gradient here.✓

(b) **(i)** time constant, τ, = CR ✓
$= 5000 \times 10^{-6} \text{ F} \times 1.2 \times 10^4 \, \Omega$
$= 60$✓ s ✓ (unit awarded mark here)

(ii) $V = V_0 \, e^{-t/RC}$ ✓
or $4.5 = 9.0 \, e^{-t/60}$
(taking logs to base e) $\Rightarrow -0.69 = -t/60$ ✓
$t = 42$ s ✓

Examiner's comment
In marking calculations of the type of (b)(ii) you are likely to score all three marks just by writing the final answer (since guessing 42 s is extremely unlikely). This means that your working will be ignored unless it is obvious that you are using a completely incorrect technique! However, you do need to include all your working in case your final answer is wrong – in which case you can gain "compensation marks" for your correct working.

Q2 How to score full marks

(a) $C = \frac{\varepsilon A}{d}$

so you could increase the capacitance by increasing the area of overlap of the plates, decreasing their separation or by inserting an insulator between them (to increase the permittivity of the dielectric). (Any **two** correct changes ✓✓)

Examiner's comment
Avoid vague answers such as "increase the size of the plates" – examiners will not know what you mean by "size" (area? volume? thickness? etc.)

(b) **(i)** $V = V_0 \, e^{-t/RC}$ ✓
$5.0 = 9.0e^{-60/RC}$ ✓
$(5.0/9.0 = 0.555 = e^{-60/RC}$
$\Rightarrow \ln(0.555) = -60/RC$
$RC = 102$ ✓
$R = 102/470 \times 10^{-6} = 220 \text{ k}\Omega$ ✓

(ii)

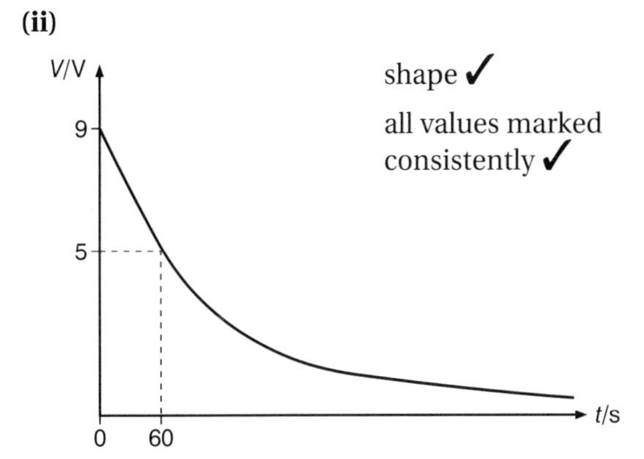

(iii) The time constant RC must be increased in order to give an increased delay. ✓This could be done by increasing the resistance of resistor R, the capacitance of capacitor C or a combination of both. ✓ ln (0.555) now must equal $-90/RC$ so $RC = 153$ s. ✓ Choosing to keep C constant (470 μF), $R = 153/470 \times 10^{-6} = 326 \text{ k}\Omega$.✓ (Keeping R constant increases C to 700 μF.)

The remaining two marks are allocated on the following basis:

Fluent, well-argued answer with accurate physics and few errors in spelling, punctuation and grammar – scores ✓✓.

Accurate physics but answer doesn't hang together well, or poor spelling, punctuation and grammar – scores ✓.

Inaccurate physics, disjointed answer and significant errors in spelling, punctuation and grammar – scores zero.

Examiner's comment
An alternative approach to **(b)(iii)** would have been to start with a higher voltage and then ensure that it reached 5 V in 90 s with the same resistor and capacitor in the circuit as previously. In this case the calculation involves calculating the initial voltage, V_i:
$5 \text{ V} = V_i e^{-90/102} = V_i(0.414) \therefore V_i = 12.1 \text{ V}.$

Chapter 6 Electromagnetism

Q1 How to score full marks

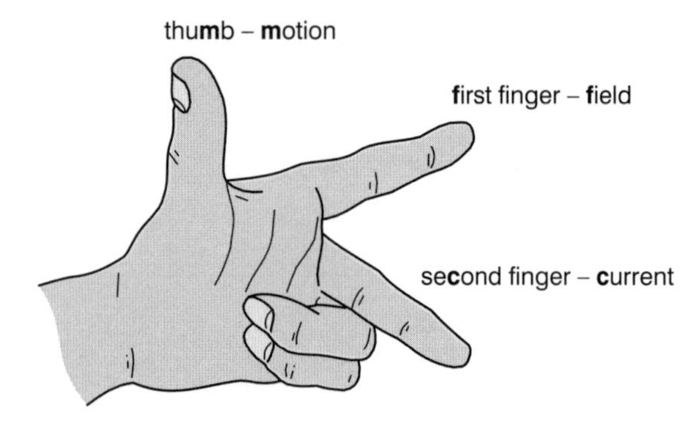

(a) **(i)** Applying Fleming's Left Hand rule to the top of the coil we see that the current goes clockwise around the coil. ✓

(ii) By applying this rule again we see that the force on the left side of the coil is to the left ✓ and that on the right side is to the right. ✓

(b) The torque = force × perpendicular distance from line of action of force to pivot. ✓
Here the perpendicular distance is zero (since force is parallel to axis of pivot) ✓
therefore there is no torque due to the forces on the vertical sides of the coil. ✓

Q2 How to score full marks

(a) The magnetic flux linkage ($N\phi$) grows (non-uniformly) as the coil enters the field. ✓
It stays constant inside the field. ✓
It then decays towards zero as the coil leaves the field. ✓

(b) When there is a change of flux linkage between a conductor and a magnetic field there will be an emf induced in the conductor ✓ such that the induced emf is proportional to the rate of change of flux linkage. ✓

(c)

induced e.m.f.

A

B

distance

Two pulses ✓ of shape similar to that shown, ✓ one positive and one negative ✓ with zero emf in the middle region. ✓

Examiner's comments
The induced emf is proportional to the rate of change of flux linkage so the speed that the coil is moved at is important here. The answer assumes that the speed is constant and so the pulses are symmetrical.
Lenz's law states that the direction of the induced emf tends to oppose the change that is inducing it and so if the first emf is chosen as being negative (arbitrary choice) the second must be positive.

Q3 How to score full marks

$$\frac{N_s}{N_p} = \frac{V_s}{V_p}$$

$$N_s = \frac{415}{11000} \times 3500 = 132$$

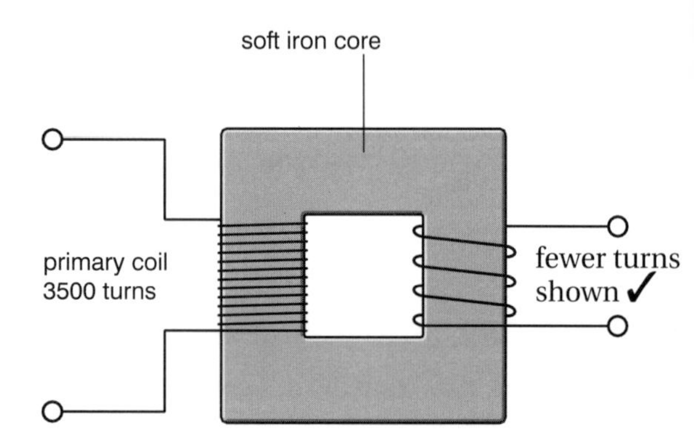

In order to induce an emf there needs to be a change of flux linkage. With d.c. this only happens at switch on or switch off. Therefore you need an a.c. supply to operate the transformer. ✓

$P = IV$

for 100% efficiency $P_p = P_s$

$\Rightarrow I_p V_p = I_s V_s$ ✓

since $\frac{V_s}{V_p} = \frac{N_s}{N_p}$

$\frac{I_p}{I_s} = \frac{N_s}{N_p}$ ✓

Any of: iron losses due to eddy currents heating the core **or** copper losses due to current heating the coil **or** hysteresis losses due to the continuous magnetisation–demagnetisation of the core. ✓

Examiner's comment
It is always good practice to get into the habit of saying where energy transfer occurs and what causes it to happen – as in the last part of this question.

Chapter 7 Radioactivity/Fission and fusion

Q1 How to score full marks

(a) (i)

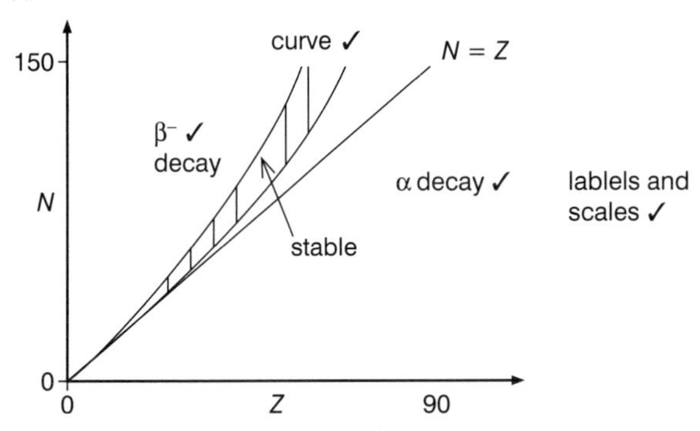

(b) (i) For an α emitter N and Z each fall by 2. ✓

(ii) For a β^- emitter N falls by 1 and Z increases by 1.✓

> **Examiner's comment**
> No explanation of these changes is required here since this is a **"State"** question.

(c) mass of atom $\propto A$ ✓

volume $= \frac{4}{3}\pi R^3$ (i.e. volume $\propto R^3$) and the equation shows that

$R \propto A^{1/3}$

so the volume $\propto A$ ✓ $\{R \propto (A^{1/3})^3\}$

$$\text{density} = \frac{\text{mass } (\propto A)}{\text{volume } (\propto A)}$$

i.e. the nucleon number (and hence the mass of the nucleus) cancels out. ✓

Q2 How to score full marks

(a) Radioactive decay occurs when an unstable nucleus emits α, β or γ radiation in order to become more stable. ✓

(b) (i) (I) activity falls from 100 → 50 in 5 s✓

(II) $\lambda = 0.69/5$ s ✓ $= 0.14$✓ s^{-1}✓

(ii) (I) Treating the area as a trapezium of side lengths 100×10^7 Bq and 57×10^7 Bq,

$$\text{area} = \frac{(100 + 57) \times 10^7 \text{ Bq}}{2} \times 4 \text{ s} ✓$$

area $= 3.14 \times 10^9$ disintegrations ✓

(II) The area represents the total number of disintegrations occurring in 4 s. ✓

$${}^{b}_{a}X \rightarrow {}^{b-4}_{a-2}Y + {}^{4}_{2}\alpha + \gamma$$

correct nucleon numbers throughout ✓

correct proton numbers throughout ✓

Chapter 9 Synoptic Questions: Comprehension Questions

Q1 How to score full marks

(a) Drilling holes in the ground is time-consuming and therefore expensive. ✓
Ores may be spread unevenly or randomly and so there is a good chance that some will be missed; therefore the technique is hit or miss. ✓

(b) (i) The mass of the ores will change the local gravitational field strength, so this field strength needs to be measured locally. ✓

> **Examiner's comment**
> You could equally well say the acceleration due to gravity would change locally. These two quantities are numerically equal but the idea of field strength will probably be better received by examiners!

(ii) The ore deposit is likely to be of higher density ✓ than other deposits and so an increased mass will produce a larger gravitational attraction in its region ✓ (by Newton's law of gravitation).

(c) Gamma ✓ radiation is most likely to be detected since it has a greater range ✓ than alpha or beta radiation (or it is less likely to be absorbed by the soil and rocks).

Q2 How to score full marks

(a) The electrodes and the soil must be in good electrical contact so that the resistance between them is very small ✓ *otherwise a significant voltage would be dropped across each electrode–soil connection.*

(b) (i) It would be advisable to drill nearer **B** ✓ because the potential gradient is less there, indicating that the soil is a better conductor ✓ than near **A**. Metal ores are likely to conduct electricity better than other deposits.

(ii) Since the graph is linear from 0–5 m (approximately) and again from 11–16 m (approximately) the edge of the body is around the 5 m ✓ mark.

(iii) Continuing the linear part from 16 m up to 20 m the voltage corresponding to 20 m is approximately 8.2 V.✓

(iv) $R = \frac{V}{I}$ ✓

$R = 8.2\ V/5 \times 10^{-3}$ A $= 1.6$ kΩ ✓ (*error carried forward for wrong V value*)

(c) This is really asking for a plot of potential gradient versus distance (for 0.5 m lengths).

The two linear portions have constant potential gradients (or values 0.45 V m^{-1} and 0.10 V m^{-1}). In the central region the potential gradient falls smoothly between these values.

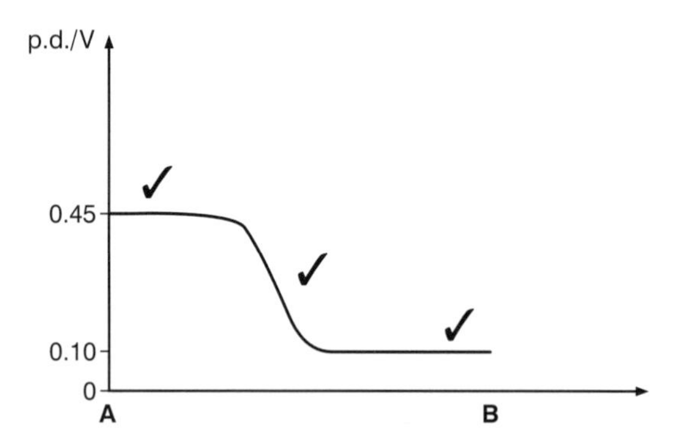

Q3 How to score full marks

(a) The explosion causes the Earth to vibrate, sending a wave out in all directions which causes the geophone to vibrate. ✓ When the geophone vibrates the magnet inside vibrates too. ✓ The mass–spring arrangement is much less rigid than the remainder of the geophone and so the mass oscillates with simple harmonic motion relative to the remainder of the geophone. ✓

(b) There is a change of flux linkage between the magnet and the coil. ✓ This will induce an emf across the coil. ✓

(c) Energy is passed from the particles near to the explosion to surrounding particles. ✓ This energy passes to particles further away ✓ as a result of transverse and longitudinal wave motion. ✓ The soft soil is much looser and less bound together than the ore deposits and so the firmer coupling in the ores means that the wave can travel faster (ore deposits are more rigid). ✓

Examiner's comment
In part(c) your "quality of written communication" is assessed. This is not simply your spelling, punctuation and grammar: your physics needs to be correct and phrased appropriately too. Your answer, as a whole, should read well to a physicist. Before you can access 2 QoWC marks you need to have scored at least 3 of the marks for physics (as in the answer given); before you can access 1 QoWC mark you will need to have scored at least 2 for the physics.

Chapter 10 Synoptic Questions: Data analysis

Q1 How to score full marks

(a) Area being calculated/counted ✓ sensible procedure used ✓

Area	A1	A2	A3	A4	A5
Time interval/s	0–0.2	0.2–0.4	0.4–0.6	0.6–0.8	0.8–1.0
Value of area	0.155	0.410	0.565	0.655	0.712
x /m	0.155	0.565	1.130	1.785	2.497

✓✓✓ for these figures or close approximations

Examiner's comment
These values will all be slight underestimates of distance x.

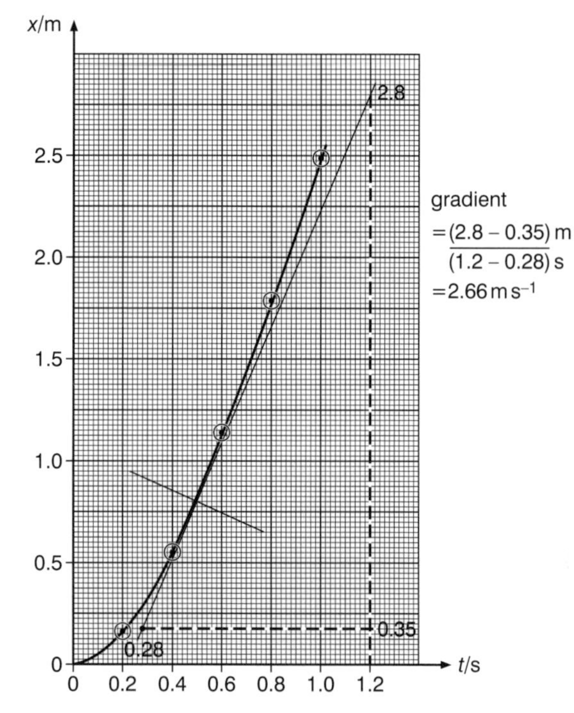

axes correctly labelled **and** units correctly labelled ✓
scales sensible and could not be doubled ✓
correctly plotted points ✓✓
curve passes through origin and reasonably smooth ✓

(b) After one second the ball bearing has fallen 2.5 ✓ m ✓.

(c) **See working on the graph**

sensible tangent ✓ of reasonable length ✓
Δx and Δt correctly recorded ✓
correct answer with candidate's data ✓
v value = 2.8 ± 0.3 ✓ m s^{-1} ✓

(d) Reading from the graph given, the velocity at 0.5 s is 2.85 ✓ $m\ s^{-1}$ ✓.

(e) Areas are slight underestimates as a result of approximating the curve with straight lines.✓ There are also judgemental decisions when estimating the values used to calculate the areas. ✓
There will be judgemental decisions regarding the best "tangent" chosen. ✓ Again, it is not possible to get totally precise values of the coordinates used to calculate the gradient of the tangent. ✓

(f)

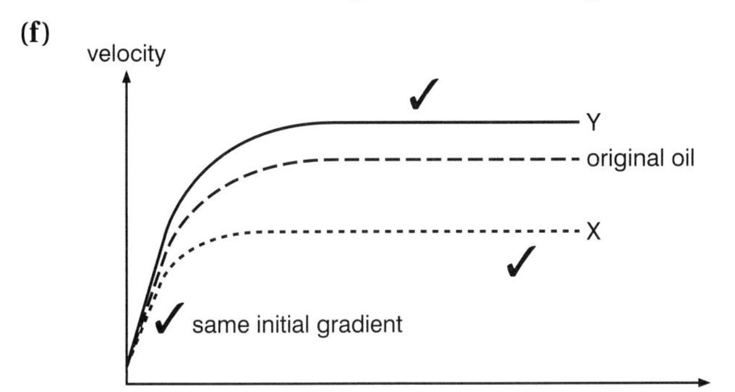

The initial gradients of each of the graphs will be the same since the ball bearings are always initially being accelerated by gravity. ✓

X will reach its terminal velocity (horizontal part of lines) in the least time since the viscous force is greatest on it. ✓

Y will do so in the longest time because with a low viscosity liquid it takes longer for the upward force to match the weight and balance it out – thus Y also has the largest terminal velocity. ✓

Chapter 11 Synoptic Questions: Structured Questions

Q1 How to score full marks

(a) **(i)** The binding energy is the energy required to separate the nucleons in the nucleus. ✓✓

(ii) The fusion of the two nuclei results in increased binding energy ✓ and increased binding energy means energy must be produced ✓ (as kinetic energy of the fusion products).

(iii) Binding energy of total of 4 nucleons in two hydrogen nuclei $= 4 \times 1$ MeV = 4 MeV. ✓

Binding energy of four nucleons in helium nucleus $= 4 \times 7$ MeV = 28 MeV. ✓

Difference in binding energy = 24 MeV. ✓

(b) **(i)** $24\ \text{MeV} = 24 \times 10^{6} \times 1.6 \times 10^{-19}\ \text{J}$
$= 3.84 \times 10^{-12}\ \text{J}$ ✓

$E = hf = \frac{hc}{\lambda}$ ✓

$3.84 \times 10^{-12}\ \text{J} = \frac{6.6 \times 10^{-34}\ \text{J s} \times 3.0 \times 10^{8}\ \text{m s}^{-1}}{\lambda}$

$\lambda = 5.2 \times 10^{-14}\ \text{m}$ ✓

(ii) $f = \frac{c}{\lambda} = \frac{3.0 \times 10^{8}\ \text{m s}^{-1}}{5.2 \times 10^{-14}\ \text{m}}$

$= 5.8 \times 10^{21}\ \text{Hz}$ ✓

$\frac{\Delta f}{f} = \frac{v}{c}$ ✓

$\Delta f = \frac{5.8 \times 10^{21}\ \text{Hz} \times 8.0 \times 10^{6}\ \text{m s}^{-1}}{3.0 \times 10^{8}\ \text{m s}^{-1}}$

$= 1.5 \times 10^{20}$ Hz decrease (since recession) ✓

Q2 How to score full marks

(a) **(i)** $E = \frac{V}{d}$ ✓

$= \frac{10\ \text{kV}}{40 \times 10^{-3}\ \text{m}}$

$= 2.5 \times 10^{5}\ \text{V m}^{-1}$ ✓

(ii) $F = Eq$ ✓
$= 2.5 \times 10^{5}\ \text{V m}^{-1} \times 3.2 \times 10^{-19}\ \text{C}$
$= 8.0 \times 10^{-14}\ \text{N}$ ✓

(iii) $qV = \frac{1}{2} mv^2$ ✓
$3.2 \times 10^{-19}\ \text{C} \times 5.0 \times 10^{3}\ \text{V} = \frac{1}{2} \times 3.4 \times 10^{-26}\ \text{kg} \times v^2$
$v = 3.07 \times 10^{5}\ \text{m s}^{-1}$ ($\approx 3.1 \times 10^{5}\ \text{m s}^{-1}$) ✓

[maximum of 5 marks for (a)]

> **Examiner's comments**
> - In part (iii) the p.d. is 5.0×10^{3}V. The ion starts at P, midway between the plates, and so is only being accelerated by half the total voltage across the plates.
> - You could work out the acceleration $a = F/m = 2.35 \times 10^{12}\ \text{m s}^{-2}$, then using $s = 20 \times 10^{-3}$ m and $u = 0$ calculate v from $v^2 = u^2 + 2as$ (it gives the same answer!!).

(b)

(i) Using Fleming's Left Hand rule the magnetic field is directed into the plane of the page. ✓

(ii) The force is always at right angles to the direction of the motion ✓ – this means that it must be centripetal and so the ion moves in a circular arc. ✓

(iii) $Bqv = \frac{mv^2}{r}$ ✓

$Bq = \frac{mv}{r}$ ✓

mv (momentum) = Bqr

Thus since B and q are constants the radius is proportional to the momentum. ✓

$$r = \frac{mv}{Bq}$$

$$r = \frac{3.4 \times 10^{-26}\ \text{kg} \times 3.1 \times 10^{5}\ \text{m s}^{-1}}{0.10\ \text{T} \times 3.2 \times 10^{-19}\ \text{C}}$$

$r = 0.33$ m ✓

(c) A greater mass means a smaller acceleration by the electric field, so the ion leaves Q with a smaller speed than before ✓ (or $qV = \frac{1}{2}mv^2$ = constant ∴ if $m\uparrow v^2\downarrow$ in the same ratio ∴ mass is dominant). This means that the ion will have a greater momentum ✓ and thus the radius of the circle will be greater. ✓

Chapter 12 Graphs and Maths

Q1 How to score full marks

By dividing throughout by T you get:

$$\frac{E}{T} = A + BT$$

so, when you plot a graph of E/T against T, it should be linear and of gradient B, y-intercept A.

E/V	0.92	2.64	5.44	9.21	14.0	19.7	27.4	35.0
T/°C	10	20	30	40	50	60	70	80
$\frac{E}{T}$/V °C^{-1}	0.092	0.132	0.181	0.230	0.280	0.328	0.391	0.437

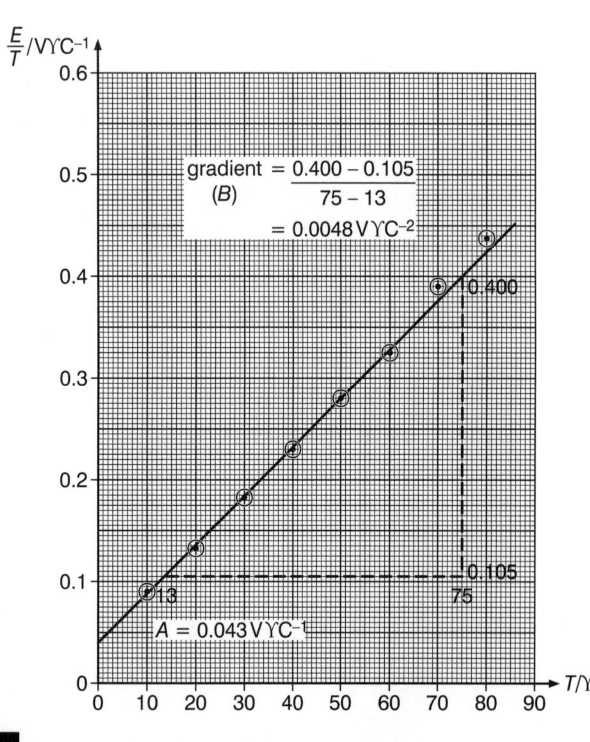

correct method – E/T values ✓

values correctly calculated ✓

all to 2/3 significant figures consistently ✓

correct axes labelled ✓

units labelled ✓

scales greater than $\frac{1}{2}$ length in each direction ✓

points correctly plotted ✓✓

best straight line ✓

overall quality of graph ✓

gradient triangle at least $\frac{1}{2}$ drawn line in each direction ✓

correct coordinates ✓

correct calculation and equated to B ✓

correct y-intercept and equated to A ✓

correct units for A (V °C^{-1}) and B (V °C^{-2}) ✓

Q2 How to score full marks

$$\ln(V) - \ln(V_0) = \frac{-t}{RC} \quad ✓$$

$$C = \frac{-t}{R\{\ln(V) - \ln(V_0)\}} \quad ✓$$

Value of C assuming no uncertainties:

$$C = \frac{-50}{1000(0.182 - 1.757)} \quad ✓$$

$C = 0.0317$ F (=31.7 mF) ✓

Value of C assuming maximum uncertainties:

[taking V_0 to be 5.6 V and V to be 1.4 V thus giving the smallest difference]

$$C_{max} = \frac{-51}{950(0.336 - 1.723)} \quad ✓✓$$

$C_{max} = 0.0387$ F (=38.7 mF) ✓

This gives an absolute uncertainty of 7.0 mF, so we should quote C as being (31.7±7.0) mF – this is a 22% uncertainty.

Q3 How to score full marks

(a) **(i)** p is the pressure in Pa, V the volume in m^3, n the number of moles, R the "universal molar ideal gas constant" in J mol^{-1} K^{-1}, T the temperature in K. (✓ all quantities, ✓ all units)

(ii) The temperatures and volumes need to be converted to K and m^3:

T/K	273	293	313	333	353	373
V^3/m^3 × 10^{-6}	40.4	42.3	46.0	49.2	52.2	55.4

temperatures all correct ✓

volumes converted ✓

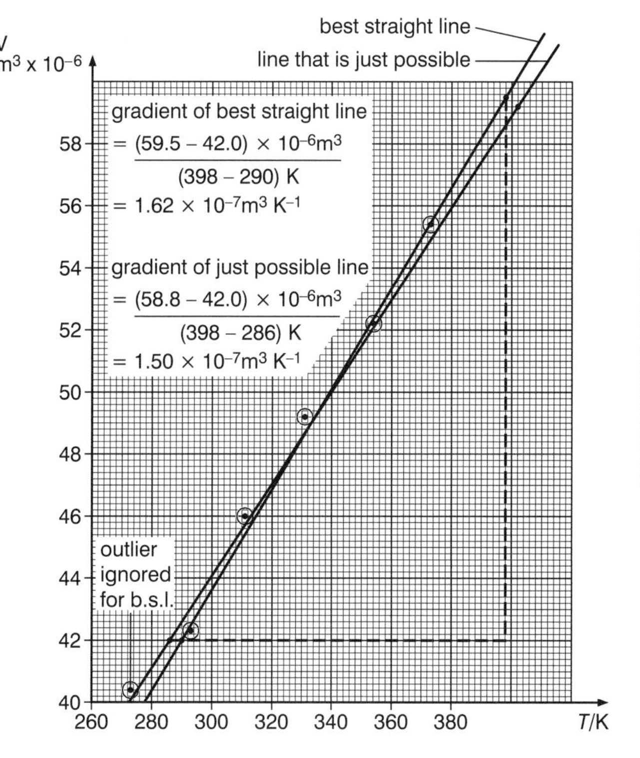

correct axes labelled ✓

units labelled ✓

scales greater than half length in each direction ✓

Examiner's comment
Notice that, in order to "fill" the page, neither axis starts from zero and the scales chosen are easy to use. It is vital not to forget that each of the volume graduations is multiplied by 10^6.

points correctly plotted ✓

best straight line ✓

overall quality of graph ✓

gradient triangle large or values well separated if not drawn in ✓

gradient correctly calculated ✓

recognition that $V = \frac{nRT}{p}$ is in the form $y = mx$

$$\frac{nR}{p} = 1.62 \times 10^{-7}\ \text{m}^3\ \text{K}^{-1}$$

so $nR = 1.62 \times 10^{-7} \times 1.1 \times 10^5$ Pa m^3 K^{-1}
$= 1.8 \times 10^{-2}$ ✓ J K^{-1} ✓ or other correct unit

Examiner's comment
It is perfectly reasonable to plot a graph of *pV* against *T* and gain full marks. The gradient will then be *nR* – which is good but you do have to multiply each value of *V* by *T* – which is time consuming!

(b) second line drawn on graph – just possible ✓

correct calculation of gradient ✓

difference between gradient equated to absolute error in nR ✓

sensible absolute error (1.2×10^{-8} m^3 K^{-1} here) ✓

Examiner's comment
In my answer I felt that the point for 273 K was anomalous (an outlier) and so, for my best straight line, I ignored this point. My line that was just possible took this point into account and so I balanced my points on either side of this just possible line including this outlier.

(c) $n = \frac{1.8 \times 10^{-2}}{8.3} = 2.17 \times 10^{-3}$ mol ✓

$n = \text{gradient} \times \frac{p}{R}$

% uncertainty in n = % uncertainty in gradient + % uncertainty in p + % uncertainty in R ✓

$= \frac{0.12}{1.62} + \frac{0.1}{1.1} + \frac{0.1}{8.3}$ ✓

$= 0.18$ ✓

$\Delta n = 0.18 \times 2.17 \times 10^{-3}$ mol ✓

$= 3.09 \times 10^{-4}$ mol ✓

NOTES